The Illustrated
Mahabharata

A Wilco Book

Outstanding works of universal interest

The Illustrated MAHABHARATA

Copyright © 2013 *Wilco*

ISBN:978-81-8252-706-5

Published by;
Wilco
Publishing House
Mumbai 400 001, India.

Tel: (91-22) 2204 1420 / 2284 2574
Fax: (91-22) 2204 1429
E mail: wilcos@vsnl.com
Web: wilcobooks.com
      wilcopicturelibrary.com

Contents

Contents

Ganesha Writes The Mahabharata

Many years ago, there lived a great sage named Ved Vyasa. He had seen the rise and fall of many Kings and Kingdoms, and was witness to several battles fought between them. One day, he decided to compose a poem based on the greatest war ever fought – the one that represented the victory of good over evil and reflected the philosophy of truth, justice and righteousness. Vyasa decided to name his glorious epic 'The Mahabharata'.

"I must preserve this sacred saga for all generations," thought Vyasa. "It will teach them the philosophy of life." So, he sat down to write the Mahabharata. But as soon as he picked up his quill, he realised that he could not compose a verse in his mind and jot it down simultaneously. By the time he wrote a verse, he would forget the next one he had in mind. "Oh, I can't write as fast as I think," Vyasa sighed sadly.

He decided to seek Lord Brahma's help and began to meditate. Pleased by his penance, Brahma appeared before him. "Be blessed, Vyasa!" said Brahma. "I am pleased that you have initiated a noble task. What can I do for you?"

"Lord, I am unable to compose and write simultaneously, please help me find someone who can write my poem without making any mistakes, as fast as I dictate it!" said Vyasa. "Pray to Lord Ganesha, the God of wisdom!" said Brahma. "He alone can write at the speed at which you speak."

Vyasa prayed to Ganesha and appeased him. "Ask what you may, O sage!" said the God of wisdom. "Please write my poem as I compose each verse in my mind, O Lord!" said Vyasa. "No bigger blessing do I desire." Ganesha willingly agreed, "However there is one condition. Once started, my quill shouldn't stop in between. You must dictate the verses quickly, one after the other."

Now Vyasa was worried because he needed time to compose the verses in his mind. So, he too, put forth a condition, "When I sing a verse to you, you must understand it first and only then write it down" Vyasa said.

Both of them agreed to the other's condition and thus began the compilation of the Mahabharata. Vyasa narrated the events in sequence, while Ganesha wrote them down without missing even a single word. After a few lines, Vyasa would compose a long and complicated couplet, so that Ganesha would take some time to understand the meaning. Meanwhile, Vyasa would compose many more verses to ensure that Ganesha's quill did not stop writing.

Ganesha wrote so fast that suddenly his quill snapped in two. Ganesha feared he would miss the words that followed. So, without wasting time, he broke off one of his tusks and began writing with it. Unaware of this, Vyasa continued to sing the verses, with his eyes closed in devotion. And thus the story went on...

～ Shantanu And Ganga ～

Once upon a time, in Northern India, there was a beautiful city named Hastinapur. It was located on the banks of the holy river, Ganga. Hastinapur was the capital of the Kingdom of King Shantanu, the mighty ruler of the Kuru Clan that belonged to the Lunar Dynasty.

King Shantanu was fond of hunting and would often linger near the Ganga. On one such day, he saw a beautiful maiden walking along the banks of the river. Shantanu instantly fell in love with her. He walked up to her and said, "I am Shantanu, the King of Hastinapur! Who are you, O fair lady, and what are you doing here?" The maiden was, in fact, Goddess Ganga herself, but she kept quiet and did not reveal her identity. Shantanu was so stunned by her beauty that he did not wait for her reply and asked, "Will you marry me?" "I will!" replied Ganga, "but I have certain conditions." "And what are they?" asked Shantanu.

Ganga said, "The first one is that you should never ask me who I am; and the second, you should allow me to do whatever I want, never question me or show your displeasure. If any of these conditions are broken, I shall leave you forever."

"I agree to all your conditions!" Shantanu said hastily, "Come, let's go to the palace!" Ganga accompanied Shantanu to his palace and soon they were married in a grand ceremony. Ganga was kind and caring; she made Shantanu's life very happy.

A year passed and Ganga delivered a baby boy. Shantanu was delighted. However, then his delight did not last long as Ganga did a strange thing. That night, Shantanu saw Ganga pick up the baby from the cradle and walk out of the palace. "Where is she going?" he wondered and followed her. Ganga went to the river and threw the child in. Watching secretly, Shantanu went pale with shock but being bound by his promise, he did not question his wife.

Another year passed and the couple had another son. This time too, Ganga threw the child into the river. Shantanu was filled with anger.

"How can a mother be so cruel to her children?" he thought, but kept his emotions in his heart and opted not to voice them. Year after year, the same thing was repeated. Each time a child was born, Ganga would throw him into the river. Seven years passed thus. Then Ganga delivered her eighth son. "Enough of this!" thought Shantanu. "I won't allow her to kill the baby this time."

So, that night, when Ganga picked up the baby and proceeded to the river, Shantanu followed her closely. As soon as she reached the river bank, Shantanu shouted, "Stop! Don't throw the baby! Who are you, ruthless woman?" Ganga turned towards him and began to weep. "Alas, my King! Now I will have to leave you," she said in a broken voice. "If only you had kept your promise!"

"How can I keep my promise when you have killed not one, but seven of my lovely sons?" Shantanu cried out in anger.

Ganga took a deep breath and said, "It's time to tell you the truth, O King. I am Ganga, and the sons born to us were Vasus, the Gods of the elements. They had been under a curse that they were to be born on earth. They requested me to be their mother and kill them the instant they were born, to rid them of the curse. This child, the eighth Vasu, is supposed to live a long and glorious life on earth. We could've stayed together... but you broke your promise and I will have to leave you now."

"No, please don't leave me alone!" Shantanu cried. He realised his mistake, but it was too late. Tears fell from his eyes as he begged Ganga to forgive him and stay. Ganga was firm in her decision. "I don't have a choice, my King!" she said, "I am taking our son with me. But I promise to return him to you when the time comes."

So saying, Ganga disappeared into the waves with the child.

With a heavy heart, Shantanu watched them vanish from his sight. Life became meaningless to him. Though he carried out his duties as a King, his mind was never at peace.

Many years passed. Shantanu often wandered near the banks of the river. "This is the only place where I find some peace," he murmured to himself. "This is where I last saw my beloved wife and son!"

On one such day, all of a sudden, he noticed a young boy shooting arrows into the river. The waves seemed to change direction according to the arrows he shot.

Shantanu was amazed at the boy's skill. "He makes the waves rise and fall!" he thought. Then to add to his wonder, Ganga appeared beside the young boy.

"This is your son, O King!" she said, smiling at Shantanu. "His name is Devavrata. He has mastered all the religious scriptures. He knows how to govern a Kingdom and is skilled in archery. In time, he will be a great warrior, a kind and wise man respected and loved by all."

Shantanu hugged Devavrata. "As promised, I have returned your son to you," said Ganga. "Now I shall take leave of both of you!" And so saying, Ganga kissed her son's forehead and disappeared. Shantanu took his son to his palace.

Devavrata was very kind and humble. His truthfulness, courage and righteousness impressed everyone. He helped his father with the day-to-day governance of the Kingdom and soon became the apple of his father's eye.

"Devavrata will prove to be an honest and sincere ruler," the King would often think.

The Supreme Oath

All was fine until one day Shantanu went hunting in the forest and saw charming young maiden named Satyavati. "Never before have I seen such beauty!" he exclaimed to himself and instantly fell in love with the young maiden. Satyavati was a fisherman's daughter. When Shantanu asked her whether she would marry him, she answered, "I would be lucky if I became your queen, but please get my father's permission first."

Shantanu went to talk to the fisherman, who was a greedy man. He wanted his daughter's future son to become the next King instead of Shantanu's son, Devavrata. When Shantanu asked for Satyavati's hand in marriage, the greedy fisherman said, "Only on the condition that the son born to you and Satyavati will succeed you to the throne!" Shantanu felt sad. "I cannot deprive my beloved Devavrata of his right to the throne!" he thought, and gave up the idea of marrying Satyavati.

Shantanu returned to the palace, but could not forget Satyavati. He was sulky and depressed. His sadness did not escape the eyes of his intelligent son. "Why is father disheartened?" he wondered. He asked the ministers and close friends of the King but no one had any clue. Then one day, Shantanu's charioteer told him about the conversation that had taken place between the greedy fisherman and the King.

Devavrata went to the fisherman and said, "My father, the King, is depressed! You have stolen his smile. Please return it to him, O fisherman; it's in your hands. As per your condition, I assure you that the throne will pass on to the son born to your daughter, Satyavati."

The greedy fisherman was still not satisfied. He asked, "Even if you forego the throne, what is the guarantee that your children and grandchildren will not aspire for it?" Devavrata replied, "Let your heart be at rest, O fisherman! My father's happiness is more valuable to me than the throne."

He then took a solemn oath, "I, Devavrata, son of King Shantanu and Goddess Ganga, pledge that I shall never marry and will never aspire for the throne of Hastinapur. Till my last breath, I shall be loyal to the throne of Hastinapur, whosoever occupies it."

There was a loud clap of thunder and the sky reverberated with Devavrata's words. Even the Gods in heaven applauded this oath and blessed Devavrata with a new name. "You shall be known as Bheeshma – the one with great determination!"

The fisherman was now content. He allowed his daughter to marry Shantanu. When Shantanu came to know of his son's supreme sacrifice, he blessed him, "You shall live as long as you desire, Bheeshma!" In a grand ceremony, Shantanu and Satyavati were married. Once again, the smile returned on Shantanu's lips and his Kingdom was a happy one.

≈ Amba Swears Revenge ≈

Queen Satyavati had two sons – Chitrangada and Vichitraveerya. Many years passed. King Shantanu died of old age. Bheeshma looked after the Kingdom until Chitrangada was old enough to be King, but the young King was killed soon after and Vichitraveerya ascended the throne.

Hastinapur flourished under Vichitraveerya's rule. During that time, the King of Kashi announced the swayamvara* of his three beautiful daughters – Amba, Ambika and Ambalika. Bheeshma decided to attend the ceremony to find a bride for Vichitraveerya and went to Kashi. Many Princes and Kings from all over the country had assembled for the swayamvara and were sitting in a large hall in the palace. When they saw Bheeshma walk in, they began to mock at him. "Isn't he the same Bheeshma who took a vow to remain a bachelor for life?" said a Prince.

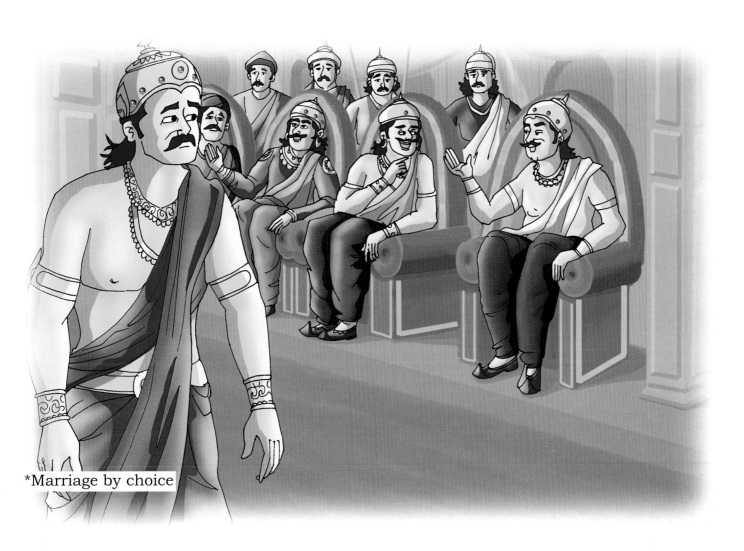

*Marriage by choice

"You're right! He is!" the other backed him. "Then what is he doing here? Has he broken his vow?" "Hahaha!" laughed the royal gathering. "Bheeshma seems to sway from his oath, since the Princesses are so beautiful!" These words pierced Bheeshma's ears. He became angry and captured Amba, Ambika and Ambalika. "King Vichitraveerya will wed all three Princesses!" he announced. "I am taking them to Hastinapur. If anyone has any objection, he will have to fight me."

The other Kings were angry. They attacked Bheeshma, but he defeated them all, including King Shalva, whom Amba secretly loved. Bheeshma then took the three Princesses with him to Hastinapur. Amba had already given her heart to Shalva, and could not forget him. She went up to Bheeshma and said, "O fair-minded son of Ganga! I have no one else but King Shalva on my mind. Is it not inappropriate to force me to marry against my wish?" Bheeshma realised his mistake and sent Amba to Shalva.

However, Amba was in for a shock when she met Shalva. "You have been won by Bheeshma," said Shalva. "I can't accept you. It is better that you return to him." Sad and disgraced, Amba returned to Hastinapur and asked Bheeshma to marry her. But Bheeshma would not break his vow. He requested Vichitraveerya to marry her, but he declined, saying, "How can I marry someone who loves another?"

Amba was aghast. She blamed Bheeshma for having ruined her life. Swearing revenge, she left Hastinapur and went to the forest. Amba began a severe penance to appease Lord Shiva and ask for the strength to kill Bheeshma. Pleased by her penance, Shiva gave her a garland and said, "Whoever wears this garland will be able to kill Bheeshma." Amba went from Kingdom to Kingdom and warrior to warrior, asking them to challenge Bheeshma. "Just wear this garland and you can defeat Bheeshma!" she would say. But even the bravest of the warriors did not dare challenge Bheeshma.

Finally, Amba reached Panchala, the Kingdom of King Drupada. But here too, she could not find a warrior brave enough to challenge and defeat Bheeshma. Feeling frustrated, Amba threw the garland on the gates of Drupada's palace and went into the forest.

Once again she meditated on Lord Shiva. This time, Shiva granted her a boon, "Amba! You shall kill Bheeshma yourself, but in your next birth!" Amba was desperate to take her revenge. She thought, "If I am to kill him in the next birth, then why should I live any longer in this one?" And she ended her life!

Amba was reborn as Shikhandi, King Drupada's daughter. One day, she saw the garland on the palace-gates and wore it. Later, Shikhandi received another boon from a God and became a man who grew up to be very intelligent and brave. Shikhandi was known as the 'strange warrior' who always wore a garland.

≈ Heir To The Throne ≈

Meanwhile in Hastinapur, in a grand ceremony, Vichitraveerya wedded Ambika and Ambalika, but soon after that, he was killed in a fierce battle. His two wives sank into depression. Adding to their agony was the fact that they did not have any children. The Kingdom of Hastinapur had no heir. Queen Satyavati was worried.

She called upon Bheeshma and said, "The throne must not be left without a ruler. Moreover, we have to save our royal lineage from extinction, O Son! Please marry your brother's wives and give an heir to Hastinapur."

But Bheeshma was not ready to compromise with his supreme oath. He asked, "Is there no other way, Mother?" "There is!" Satyavati replied in a grave tone. "Perhaps, we are left with only one option."

She then elaborated, "Long before my marriage, a sage named Parashar blessed me with a son, none other than the great Sage Vyasa. He alone can help us in this hour of peril." Bheeshma agreed and Satyavati called upon Sage Vyasa. "Hastinapur longs for an heir, O Vyasa," Satyavati said with tears in her eyes. "Use your celestial powers and bless the childless widows of your brother with sons."

Following his mother's orders, Vyasa went to see Ambika and Ambalika. Now it so happened that after having spent many years as a hermit, Vyasa looked untidy and ugly. The moment Ambika saw him, she closed her eyes. Vyasa blessed her with a son but, unfortunately, the child born was blind. He was named Dhritarashtra. Next, he went to see Ambalika. As soon as Ambalika saw the unkempt sage, she turned pale with shock and fear. She too, was blessed with a son, but the child born to her was lean and pale. He was named Pandu. Satyavati felt sad to see that both the babies were not normal.

She urged Vyasa that he should see Ambalika once more and bless her with another son, this time, hopefully, a healthy one. Ambalika had no desire to face the sage again, but she couldn't refuse the Queen's orders. So, she asked one of her faithful maids to put on her royal garb and sit in her place. When Vyasa came to Ambalika's chamber, he didn't realise that it was the maid, as she had partly covered her face with a veil. Vyasa blessed the maid, thinking that she was Ambalika. A beautiful son was born to the maid. He was named Vidura. "This child will be just, sincere and intelligent," blessed Vyasa and took leave.

Dhritarashtra, Pandu, and Vidura were brought up together. They loved and respected each other. Till the boys grew up, Bheeshma administered the day-to-day affairs of the court. When Pandu was old enough to rule, he was crowned King, as his elder brother, Dhritarashtra, was blind. Vidura, the wisest of all was chosen as the Prime Minister. Bheeshma helped and guided the King and his ministers.

The Sage Curses Pandu

One day, Bheeshma thought, "Dhritarashtra and Pandu are well settled now. I must get them married." Mother Satyavati also was of the same opinion and so, Bheeshma began his search for suitable alliances for the two Princes.

Soon, Dhritarashtra was married to Gandhari, the beautiful and chaste daughter of the King of Gandhar. When Gandhari came to know of Dhritarashtra's blindness, she opted to be blindfolded for life. "I shall not enjoy anything that my dear husband is deprived of, be it eyesight or anything else!" she declared. Since that day, this devoted lady always tied a piece of cloth over her eyes. Pandu had two wives – Kunti, the daughter of King Kuntibhoja, and Madri, the beautiful Princess of the Madra Kingdom. All went well and Hastinapur progressed on the path to prosperity.

Pandu was fond of hunting and would often go on hunting expeditions. On one such expedition, he rode deep into the forest. Suddenly, he saw a pair of deer resting behind a bush. Pandu shot an arrow at one of the deer. As soon as the arrow pierced the deer, it cried out in a human voice, "Aaaaaargh!" Pandu was shocked to see that the deer had been transformed into a sage. Actually, the two deer were a sage and his wife. They were resting in the quiet of the forest.

Pandu realised his mistake and ran to help the sage, but it was too late. "Your arrow has fatally wounded me! What wrong did I do to you? I was just resting with my wife. You have killed me for no reason!" cried the sage. And then he cursed Pandu, "You shall die if you touch your wife or come close to her." Pandu sank into depression. He returned to the palace with a heavy heart and a restless mind. Kunti and Madri noticed his dejection and wished to know the reason.

Pandu then narrated all that had happened. "I have to live with this curse throughout my life," he sobbed. The next day, Pandu handed over his crown to Dhritarashtra and renounced his kingship. "I have no right to lead this royal life; I have sinned!" he declared.

Kunti and Madri too followed their husband's decision and renounced all their luxuries and comforts. The three left the palace and went to live in the forest.

Life in the forest was peaceful but Pandu still remained restless. "My name will die with me," he thought sadly, "I shall never have sons to carry my name." Day by day, his health began to deteriorate.

His two wives could only watch him sulk. "There's nothing we can do, sister," they would say to each other.

≈ Surya's Son Is Born ≈

One day, Kunti remembered a boon she had obtained in her childhood. Kunti was the adopted daughter of King Kuntibhoja. She had been a pleasant child and everyone would sing her praises. One day, when Kunti was a young girl, Sage Durvasa, who was known for his short temper, paid a visit to King Kuntibhoja's court. Kunti was delegated with the duty to look after the sage and ensure that his stay in the palace was comfortable.

Kunti performed her duty extremely well and made a very good impression on the sage. Before Durvasa left, he granted a unique boon to Kunti. "I shall teach you a sacred verse, dear Kunti!" he said. "Meditate on any God of your choice and chant this verse; you will be blessed with a child by that God, and the child will have all the qualities of that God." Durvasa then taught Kunti the sacred verse and took leave.

Kunti was so thrilled with her boon that she could not wait to use it. In her childishness, she chanted the verse while gazing at the sun. Before she realised it, the Sun God, Surya, appeared before her. "Dear Kunti," said Surya, "I shall give you a beautiful son as you so desired!" Kunti was taken aback. "No, no. Please don't!" she cried. "I don't desire a child; I was just testing my boon."

"The power of the sacred verse cannot be reversed," said Surya. "I must give you a child since you have invoked me." "But how can I become a mother?" Kunti said, horrified. "I am as yet unmarried! Bearing a child will bring a bad name to me and my family!"

There was nothing Surya could do to reverse the boon. The next moment, he blessed Kunti with a divine child. The boy wore a gold armour and earrings. Kunti looked at the child with awe and surprise.

"His armour and earrings shall ensure his invincibility!" said Surya and disappered. Kunti was left alone with her child. She was scared to carry the baby home. Recluctantly, after thinking about the consequences she decided to abandon him.

"It's sad but I have no choice," thought the young girl. She knew she had committed a grave mistake in her foolishness and haste. With a heavy heart and tearful eyes, Kunti wrapped the baby in a silk cloth, put him in a basket and carried him to the river.

On reaching the banks, she caressed her son once again. "Forgive me, O my son," she sobbed, "and forgive me, God, for the sin I am about to commit!" Then she set the basket afloat on the river. The waves slowly carried away her baby out of sight.

Recalling the sorrowful event after so many years, Kunti was filled with remorse. But suddenly her eyes brightened with hope. "Now is the right time to use my boon," she thought, smiling.

Birth of The Pandavas

Kunti at once went to Pandu and said, "Don't be disheartened, my Lord! We can still have children." "How?" Pandu asked anxiously. "By way of a special boon granted to me by Sage Durvasa!" replied Kunti. "I know a sacred verse by which I can invoke any God and beget a child from him." Pandu was thrilled to hear this. "You have given me a reason to live, Kunti!" he said. "Please use your boon right away."

Kunti sat under a tree and began to meditate. She first invoked Lord Dharma, the God of justice. As soon as Kunti chanted the sacred verse, Dharma appeared before her. "Be blessed, Kunti!" said Dharma and granted her a beautiful son. "He shall be just and righteous, and shall never stray from the truth," said Dharma and disappeared. Kunti began to meditate again, this time upon Lord Vayu, the God of wind. Vayu too blessed her with a son.

"This child will have the strength of a thousand elephants," said Vayu. Next, Kunti invoked Lord Indra, the King of Gods, and begot her third son. Indra blessed the child and said, "He will be an invincible warrior and the best archer of all time."

After thus getting three sons, Kunti taught the sacred verse to Madri. Madri meditated upon the twin Gods, the Ashwins, the physicians to the Gods. Instantly, the Ashwins appeared before her and blessed her with two beautiful sons. "The boys will be very handsome and intelligent, and will have the power of healing," said the Ashwins.

In this way, Pandu had five sons. Dharma's son, the eldest, was named Yudhishthira, Vayu's son Bheema, Indra's son Arjuna, and the Ashwins' sons were named Nakula and Sahdeva. They were collectively called the Pandavas. Pandu, Kunti and Madri were proud parents; their happiness revolved around their five sons. Never again was Pandu sad or depressed.

One day, in his joy, he even forgot the sage's curse, and touched Madri, and as fate would have it, the curse came into effect. Then and there, Pandu breathed his last. Madri couldn't bear this sorrow and ended her life.

Kunti was left alone with five sons. She resolved to bring them up in such a way that they would bring pride to their father's and forefathers' names. Kunti and the Pandavas were still living in the forest when some sages advised them to return to Hastinapur. Kunti followed their advice and returned to at the palace with five sons.

Bheeshma and King Dhritarashtra, though saddened with the loss of Pandu and Madri, gladly welcomed Pandu's children. Gandhari hugged Kunti and consoled her. "You have suffered a lot, dear Kunti!" she said. "No more of it! We are all here to support you."

The Jealous Kauravas

Meanwhile, Dhritarashtra and Gandhari were blessed with a hundred sons, collectively called the Kauravas. Kunti was overjoyed to see the Kauravas. "I feel as if I have not just five, but a hundred and five sons," she said. Gandhari too, loved the Pandavas as much as her own sons.

All the Princes grew up together. Their grandsire Bheeshma arranged for their education and other requirements. The royal teacher of Hastinapur, Kripacharya, was entrusted with the job of teaching the religious scriptures to the Princes. As the boys grew up, Bheeshma noticed that the Pandavas were becoming an eyesore to the Kauravas. The eldest Kaurava, Duryodhana, was selfish and overambitious right from his childhood. He had enjoyed the status of 'the eldest Prince' before the arrival of the Pandavas. But now, Yudhishthira, being older to Duryodhana, was considered 'the eldest Prince'.

However, that was not acceptable to Duryodhana. He became jealous of the Pandavas and would often ask Bheeshma, "Grandsire! Why didn't you stop the King, my father, from accepting the Pandavas and allowing them into our palace? They have come here only to usurp the throne that should come to me after my father."

Bheeshma would chide him, "You shouldn't think ill of the Pandavas, Duryodhana! They are your brothers." But Duryodhana still hated the Pandavas.

Although they lived and played together, the Kauravas were always looking for an opportunity to harm the Pandavas. Bheema was the strongest of them all and loved food more than anything else.

So one day, Duryodhana planned to kill Bheema and offered him a bowl of pudding that had been poisoned.

After Bheema had the pudding and became unconscious, Duryodhana with the help of Dushasana tied his hands and feet and threw him into a river. Bheema sank to the riverbed where there were hundreds of snakes. As the snakes began to bite Bheema, the poison in his body was sucked out and he soon regained consciousness. The King of the snakes became so fond of Bheema that he gave him many bowls of nectar to drink. With each bowl of nectar that Bheema drank, he gained more and more strength and power. Thus he acquired great strength and came out of the river.

In the palace, Kunti and the other Pandavas were worried that Bheema had gone missing. They searched for him everywhere. Just then Bheema returned. Kunti was glad to see him safe. Bheema then narrated to them all that had happened. He wanted to punish Duryodhana, but Kunti advised him to calm down and forget the matter. A bitter situation was thus avoided due to Kunti's wisdom. However, a rivalry between the two groups of cousins had started to take shape.

⁀ A Divine Child Is Born ⁀

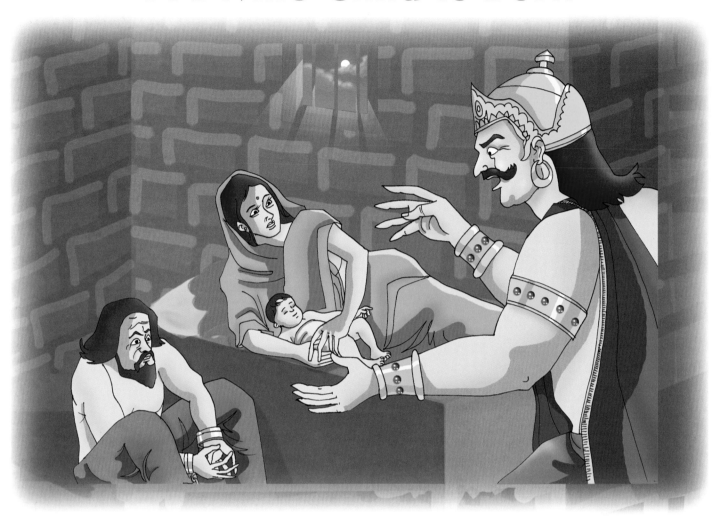

While all this was happening in Hastinapur, a divine child was born in a prison in the not-very-far-off city of Mathura. The child, Krishna, was believed to be the eighth incarnation of Lord Vishnu, who had manifested on earth to check the growth of evil and to re-establish faith, justice and righteousness. Krishna's maternal uncle, Kamsa, the King of Mathura, was very cruel and tyrannical. He was invincible and much feared by all. He had imprisoned his old father, Ugrasena, and usurped the throne.

One day, it was prophesied that Kamsa would be killed by the eighth son of his sister, Devaki, who was married to Vasudeva. Since then, Kamsa had imprisoned Devaki and Vasudeva and kept a close watch on them. Whenever Devaki delivered a child, Kamsa would instantly kill the baby. This catastrophe was repeated seven times.

However, when Devaki gave birth to her eighth son, Krishna, a divine voice prompted Vasudeva to carry the baby to a village named Gokul and exchange him with the just-born daughter of another couple, Nanda and Yashoda. It was impossible to carry the baby out of the prison, but suddenly, as if by some miracle, all the guards fell asleep and the gates of the dungeon swung open. Carrying the infant in a basket, Vasudeva instantly rushed out. He had to return with Nanda's daughter before Kamsa came to know of the birth of Krishna.

Gokul lay across the river Yamuna. As soon as Vasudeva reached the banks of Yamuna, there arose a terrible storm. Vasudeva waded into the river. Suddenly, it began to rain heavily. "Oh, the level of the water is rising; how will I cross the river?" Vasudeva thought, finding it difficult to walk against the current. At the same time, he was also worried that the baby would get drenched in the rain. Just then Adi Sesha, the snake of Lord Vishnu, rose from the river and spread its hood over the child, protecting it from the rain. The river parted thereby creating a path for Vasudeva to go across.

Thus, aided by divine intervention, Vasudeva reached Nanda's house, exchanged Krishna for Nanda's daughter, and returned to Mathura. The minute he entered the dungeon, the doors miraculously banged shut and the guards woke up.

Seeing the baby, one of the guards hurried to inform Kamsa. In no time, the cruel King stormed into Devaki's cell and grabbed the baby. "Spare this child, O brother! She is a girl; you are under no threat from her," Devaki pleaded. But Kamsa had no mercy. He dashed the baby onto the floor. She was transformed into a fierce Goddess and thundered, "Beware, Kamsa! Your destroyer is safe in Gokul," and then disappeared. Kamsa was horrified. He sent his men to Gokul to kill all the boys born on that date, but Krishna was destined to survive as he had to fulfill the prophecy and slay Kamsa. So, at the time when the Pandavas were growing up in Hastinapur, Krishna was growing up in Gokul with his foster parents.

᨝ Vasusena ᨝

Around the same time, but at a different place, another miracle child was also growing up. He was none other than Kunti's son from Surya, the child that Kunti had abandoned in the river. The child had been discovered by a charioteer named Adhiratha, who was childless. "At last, my prayers have been answered!" thought Adhiratha and carried the baby home to his wife, Radha. They believed that the child was sent by the Gods, and happily accepted him as their own. The child was named Vasusena and was also called Radheya, which meant 'son of Radha'.

Vasusena grew up to be intelligent and brave. Right from his childhood, he showed no interest in becoming a charioteer like his father; instead, he had an urge to hold a bow and arrow! One day, the boy candidly asked to his mother. "Mother, why do I get dreams of battles and wars? Why do I crave to hold weapons and fight? Am I different from you and father? Is there something wrong with me?"

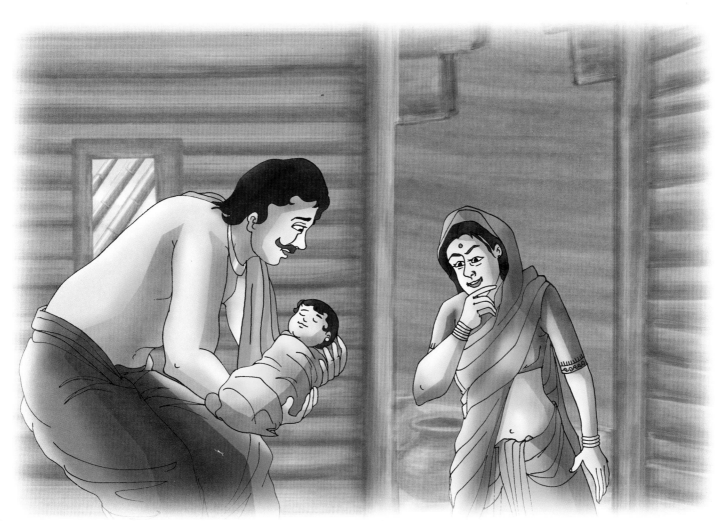

Radha hugged her son and said, "Nothing is wrong with you, Vasusena! But there is something you should know now." "What, mother?" Vasusena asked anxiously. Radha replied, "You are not our own son! We found you in a basket afloat in the river. That is why your habits and characteristics are different from that of your father's." Vasusena was stunned. "Whose son am I then?" he asked. "That we don't know, son! We believe you are the son of the Gods, sent to us in your golden armour and earrings. We were childless, and you came to us like a boon." Saying this, Radha burst into tears.

Vasusena fell at Radha's feet and said, "You and you alone are my mother. I don't know any other parents apart from you both! I shall always be known as the son of Radha and Adhiratha." Radha was overwhelmed. Thereafter, Adhiratha and Radha acknowledged Vasusena's wishes and interests, and raised him as a warrior instead of a charioteer, coaching him in martial arts and warfare.

~ Acharya Drona ~

Meanwhile in Hastinapur, the Pandava and Kaurava Princes had started their education and training in sports.

One day, as they were playing in the garden, their ball fell into a well. The boys, not knowing what to do, gathered around and stood there looking into it. Just then, there came a stranger. Seeing the children confused and worried, the stranger asked, "What's the matter, children? Why do you look so distressed?"

Yudhishthira replied, "Our ball has fallen into the well and we don't know how to take it out." The stranger peeped into the well and spotted the ball. "Haha! Is that all?" he laughed softly. "Let me help you!" He picked up a blade of grass and aiming it at the ball inside.

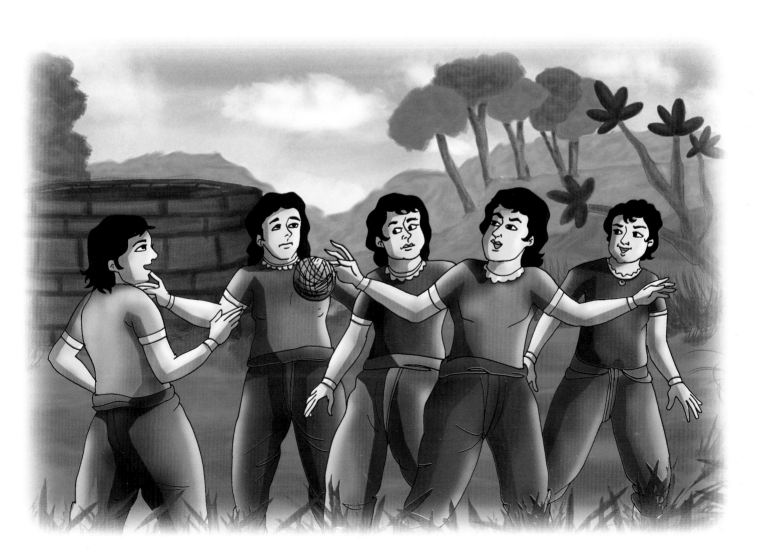

As the children watched in awe, the stranger took a fistful of blades of grass and threw them in, one by one. Each blade stuck to the previous one and a chain of grass was formed. The stranger then began to pull the chain slowly and in no time, the ball was out! The Princes danced with joy. Some of them ran into the palace to tell Grandsire Bheeshma about the stranger who had pulled out their ball almost miraculously.

"He is no ordinary man, Grandsire!" said Yudhishthira. "Even a tender blade of grass becomes a sharp arrow in his hands." "Such an extraordinary feat!" Bheeshma thought. "It can be none other than the great Acharya* Drona!"

Led by Yudhishthira, Bheeshma came to the place where the stranger stood surrounded by the Princes. He had guessed right! The stranger was indeed Acharya Drona, one of the greatest of warriors and teachers in those days. He also happened to be Kripacharya's brother-in-law .

*Teacher

Drona had come to visit King Dhritarashtra. Bheeshma gave him a warm welcome. "Hastinapur is honoured to have you here, Acharya Drona!" he said. Then Bheeshma made a request. "You are adept at various forms of martial arts and are the supreme authority in archery. I shall be grateful to you if you would train the Princes in warfare."

Drona agreed and started a school near the city. Soon his fame spread far and wide. Many children, besides the Princes of Hastinapur, came to study and learn under Drona.

Drona was a brilliant teacher. His students were free to choose the weapon they wished to learn. Yudhisthira chose the sword and the javelin, Bheema and Duryodhana selected the mace, Arjuna picked up a bow and arrows, and likewise all the others chose the weapon they liked most.

≈ The Best Archer ≈

Arjuna would practice archery with great concentration and perseverance. Acharya Drona was very pleased with Arjuna and would often declare Arjuna as his best student.

This made Duryodhana and his brother, Dushasana extremely jealous. One day they openly criticized Drona, accusing him of favouritism. "We are no less skillful than Arjuna!" said Duryodhana. "Then why do you give preference to Arjuna? And why do you profess that Arjuna is the best?"

Drona decided to prove to them that Arjuna was indeed, the best. So, he asked all the students to prepare for a test of archery. On the stipulated day, all the students gathered around their guru*. Drona had placed a wooden bird on the branch of a distant tree.

*Teacher

A prominent artificial eye was painted on the wooden bird. Drona called all his disciples and, pointing to the wooden bird, told them, "Look there...children... a bird is sitting on that tree. You have to hit the eye of the bird with your arrow. Are you ready?" All the children nodded.

First it was Yudhishthira's turn. He stretched his bow-string and was about to release the arrow when Dronacharya asked him, "Before you shoot, O eldest son of Kunti, tell me what you see at this point?" Yudhishthira replied, "O Gurudev*! I see you, the tree, my brothers, and the bird!"

This was not the answer Drona was looking for. He smiled and asked Yudhishthira to step aside. "Your turn, Bheema!" he said. When Bheema had taken his position and stretched his bow-string, Drona asked, "Tell me, what do you see?" "I see the sky, the leaves, and the bird!" "You too, step aside, Bheema!" said Drona. He asked the same question to Duryodhana, Nakula, Sahdeva and many others.

*Respected Teacher

But none of them gave him a satisfactory reply. Finally, Drona asked Arjuna to step forward and take position. "Tell me, Arjuna, what do you see?" "Nothing but the bird's eye, O Gurudev!" replied Arjuna. "Then shoot, my son!" Drona said happily, at last getting the response he was looking for.

Arjuna's arrow flew with a twang and hit the bird's eye. Now Drona addressed the gathering, "None of you but Arjuna saw the target; his concentration was focused only on the bird's eye. The rest of you would have missed your target because you had poor concentration."Drona then turned to Duryodhana and said, "Now you know why I say that Arjuna is my best student?"

Duryodhana, blinded by jealousy, refused to see the point. He still felt that Drona was unduly favouring Arjuna.

≈ Ekalavya's Sacrifice ≈

Meanwhile, unknown to Drona himself, another supreme archer was in the making. His name was Ekalavya and he lived near Drona's ashram*, where the Princes took lessons in the various arts of warfare.

For quite a few days, Ekalavya had been watching Drona instruct his students. One day, the little boy went to his mother and said, "O mother, I have a great desire to learn the art of archery from Acharya Drona. Please get me admission in his ashram." "We belong to a lower caste, Ekalavya," said his mother, "and so Acharya Drona will not accept you as his disciple. Give up your dream, my son!" But Ekalavya was determined. "So what if Acharya Drona doesn't accept me as his disciple?" he said. "I have already accepted him as my guru!" Ekalavya made a clay idol of Drona and installed it under a tree near his house. Every morning and evening, he worshipped the idol as his guru and in front of it, taught himself archery.

*Hermitage

He hid behind the trees and learnt the skills that Drona demonstrated to his disciples. The talented young boy soon acquired great knowledge in archery. He could shoot arrows as perfectly as Drona himself. Though it was all self-learnt, this humble disciple attributed his success to his guru.

One day, it so happened that Drona and Arjuna were passing by Ekalavya's house. It was calm and peaceful all around as the people were taking their afternoon nap. Suddenly, the tranquility was broken by the barking of a dog. Somewhere nearby, Ekalavya had been practicing his archery. He was so annoyed by the constant barking of the dog that he shot an arrow that sealed the dog's mouth, without hurting the dog. When Drona and Arjuna saw the dog with his mouth sealed with an arrow, they were stunned. "Only a truly great archer can shoot an arrow with such expertise," Drona exclaimed. "But who could that be?" They started searching for the person who had shot the arrow.

They saw the young Ekalavya practicing archery. When Ekalavya saw Drona, he fell prostrate before him, saying, "Welcome, O Gurudev!" Drona was surprised when Ekalavya called him his guru. "Why do you call me your guru, dear boy?" asked Drona. "Because I have learnt archery from you, Gurudev!" replied Ekalavya. "But I never taught you!" said Drona. "You did!" Ekalavya smiled.

He then led Drona and Arjuna to the spot where he had installed Drona's idol. It took no time for Drona to realise that Ekalavya was even superior to Arjuna in the skills of archery. The guru became worried. "If this boy could learn so much by himself, then he is a threat to Arjuna! I can't let anyone else become the best archer on this earth." The guru was crafty and decided to remove Arjuna's competitor from the scene. Smiling at Ekalavya, Dronacharya said, "You say that I am your guru. Then as is customary, won't you give me some guru-dakshina*?"

*Fee

Ekalavya was overwhelmed, he said, "I feel blessed that you have accepted me as your disciple. Whatever you ask of me is yours." "Then give me the thumb of your right hand as guru-dakshina!" demanded Drona. Arjuna was shocked at this. How could the boy shoot arrows if he gave away the thumb of his right hand? But that was exactly what Drona wished for – that Ekalavya would never be able to hold an arrow.

Ekalavya also knew the consequences of giving such a guru-dakshina, but his love and devotion for his guru was so great that he showed no hesitation and in an instant, cut off his right thumb and placed it at the feet of Drona. "Here, O Gurudev! Please accept my humble guru-dakshina," said the brave boy. Standing aside, Arjuna witnessed the supreme sacrifice. Even the Gods in the heaven praised the greatness of Ekalavya. Drona felt very guilty for having demanded such a heavy price from an innocent disciple. However, he was glad that he had succeeded in protecting the status of his favourite disciple, Arjuna.

⌇ Parashurama Curses Karna ⌇

Far away from Arjuna, his half-brother, Vasusena, was growing up with his charioteer parents, Adhiratha and Radha. Although his parents trained him to be a warrior, Vasusena also had a burning desire to learn the religious scriptures. His parents advised him to go to the ashram of Parashurama, the Guru of Brahmins. When Vasusena reached the ashram of Parashurama, he was told that Parashurama would teach only Brahmin boys. So, Vasusena disguised himself as a Brahmin boy and entered the ashram. Guru Parashurama accepted him as his disciple and gave him a new name – Karna. Thus Karna began to learn the religious scriptures – the Vedas and the Upanishads.

Time passed; Karna grew up. He was sincere and hard-working and soon became Guru Parashurama's favourite student. One day, Parashurama was resting under a tree with his head on Karna's lap.

Soon, he fell asleep. Meanwhile, a big insect started biting Karna's thigh. Karna felt agonizing pain; he clenched his fists and ground his teeth, but did not even wince for fear of waking his master. As the insect continued to bite Karna, blood started to ooze from the wound. Karna still, did not move; he sat still enduring all the pain. The blood trickled out and flowed down his thigh, soon reaching Parashurama's cheek.

Feeling the warm blood, Parashurama woke up with a start. "What is this, Karna? You are bleeding! Why didn't you say anything?" asked Parashurama. Karna said, biting his lips suppressing pain, "I did not wish to wake you, Gurudev!" Parashurama was amazed at Karna's ability to endure pain. Then a thought struck him. "No Brahmin can bear pain like this! Karna may not be a Brahmin!" Filled with suspicion, Parashurama asked, "Who are you actually?"

Karna could not lie to his Guru any more. He bowed down his head in shame and said, "I am no Brahmin, but the son of a charioteer." Parashurama was enraged. "You liar!" he yelled at Karna. "How dare you join my ashram under false pretexts?" Karna fell at his feet and begged, "Please forgive me! I only wished to learn from the greatest guru of all times!"

No apology could appease Parashurama. He withdrew his feet from Karna's hands and said, "Although you were my best disciple, the fact remains that you have deceived me. Hence, O Karna, I curse you that you shall forget the mantra* for invoking the Brahmastra** when you need it the most! Since you have learned by deception, your knowledge will desert you at your most desperate hour!"

Karna was horrified, he begged for mercy. But Parashurama was relentless and threw Karna out of his ashram.

*Sacred chant **Special weapon granted by Lord Brahma himself

Drona's Revenge

Meanwhile, the Kauravas and Pandavas finished their training under Acharya Drona. It was time for their guru to ask for guru-dakshina. "All the students wondered what their Guru would ask for." Just then Drona addressed them, "My boys, it's time for a real mission. Let me te you something about myself first."

He then narrated, "When I was a student, I had a friend named Drupada, who was the Prince of Panchala. We grew up together, and became very good friends. Drupada promised me that when he would become the King, he would give me half of his Kingdom. Time passed, we completed our studies and training. Drupada became the King of Panchala while I became an expert in archery and decided to become a teacher. Soon I was married to Kripi, sister of Kripacharya, the royal teacher of Hastinapur."

The boys listened attentively as their guru narrated his story.

"We had a son named Ashwatthama," Drona continued, "We faced hard times and lived in poverty. One day, I remembered my friend Drupada's promise. With hope in my heart, I went to meet him and sought his help. But instead of helping me, Drupada refused to even recognize me. When I told him that we were the best of friends, he laughed and said that a poor Brahmin and a King could never be friends. Feeling humiliated and sad, I returned home. Then I shifted my family to the Kingdom of Hastinapur and went to meet King Dhritarashtra – that day when you were all playing and your ball had fallen into the well. What happened after that is known to you all. I am grateful to the destiny that gave me the opportunity to teach such bright and worthy pupils like you, dear Princes. Now I shall ask one favour from you. I know you won't let me down in any way!"

"Command us, O Gurudev!" the Princes cried in unison.

First, Drona called the Kauravas and said, "I want you to capture King Drupada for me!" The Kauravas set off, with Duryodhana in the lead. They attacked the Kingdom of Panchala and fought hard, but Drupada's army proved stronger and the Kauravas had to retreat.

Next, Drona summoned the Pandavas and assigned them the same task. The Pandavas set off to fight Drupada and his army. In the fierce fight that followed, Arjuna and his army defeated the soldiers of Panchala and captured Drupada. The triumphant Pandavas returned to their guru.

"We have accomplished the task, Gurudev!" cried Arjuna. "Here's King Drupada, just like you asked for!" Drona was pleased. "I knew you would do me proud, my boys!" he smiled.

Then he turned to Drupada, who stood there defeated, tied with ropes around his body.

"I do not wish to kill you, Drupada," said Drona, "I just want to remind you of your promise, the one that you made to me when we were students." Drupada was angry, but he also knew that he had betrayed Drona and so, had invited trouble. If Drona so wanted, he could now keep the entire Kingdom of Panchala. But he, being fair, released the King and returned half his Kingdom. "Half your Kingdom belongs to me, Drupada! Do you remember your promise or shall I remind you again?" said Drona. Drupada had no other choice but to agree, but in his heart, he vowed to take revenge on Drona some day. After returning to his Kingdom, Drupada remained restless.

On one side, he wanted to avenge the insult, while on the other, he was so impressed by Arjuna's prowess that he wished to have a daughter so he could get her married to Arjuna. To fulfil his wishes, Drupada performed a yagna* and prayed for a son to kill Drona, and a daughter, who would marry Arjuna! His prayers bore fruit and he was blessed with a son, Drishtidyumna, and a daughter, Draupadi.

*Sacrifice

The Festival of Competitive Sports

In the meantime, the Kaurava and Pandava Princes had returned to Hastinapur. Bheeshma, Vidura, Gandhari and Kunti gave them a warm welcome. Kunti was overwhelmed to see her children grown into healthy and powerful adults. Gandhari hugged her sons and blessed them. After the religious rituals, the Princes were led into the palace.

Soon, a great festival of competitive sports was held in honour of the young Princes. The citizens gathered in the palace grounds to watch the event. "Our young Princes have mastered the various forms of martial arts and warfare!" said one man. "Yes, friend!" nodded the other. "They have been trained by the great Acharya Drona. Today they will display their skill and talent!" Bheeshma, Dhritarashtra, Gandhari, Kunti, Vidura, Kripacharya, and many others graced the auspicious occasion with their presence.

Acharya Drona himself, was present to judge and reward the best candidate. One by one, the Princes came forward and exhibited their skills. Yudhishthira was a skilled charioteer. Duryodhana and Bheema were masters of mace fighting. Nakula and Sahdeva proved to be experts with their swords. Dushasana and his younger brothers also performed amazing feats with their weapons.

It soon became obvious that Arjuna's talent was by far the most superior. The entire gathering watched spellbound as Arjuna shot an arrow into the sky and brought down rain. He let loose a shower of arrows and built a bridge. He shot out fiery arrows, which produced water from their tips. Arjuna attracted the most cheers and applause. Drona was highly impressed and was just about to announce Arjuna's name as the 'best sportsman' when suddenly a voice called out loudly, "Don't be so hasty in declaring the best sportsman!" Everyone turned in the direction of the voice.

It was Karna, the mighty son of Surya, standing tall in his magnificent golden armour. "Who is he?" the people asked each other and exclaimed, "He looks so handsome and fearless! We have never seen him before!" The members of the royal family were surprised, too. "I know Arjuna is a great warrior, O Acharya Drona!" said Karna. "But I can prove that I am no less!" Saying this, Karna began to perform the same feats with his bow and arrows that Arjuna had displayed.

He challenged Arjuna to compete with him. Now Drona became worried. He feared that this strange warrior might defeat his beloved disciple Arjuna and steal the show. He thought of a plan to keep Arjuna's competitor at bay. Drona stood up and addressed to Karna. "Who are you, O stranger? How dare you challenge Prince Arjuna without disclosing your identity? Don't you know that a common man cannot challenge a member of the royal lineage?" Karna was silent.

Drona again asked, "Which royal family do you belong to? Are you a Prince? Arjuna is a Prince, he can only compete with another Prince. Tell us who you are." Karna continued to remain silent.

At this, the jealous Duryodhana saw a great opportunity to humiliate Arjuna. "I am sure this strange warrior can defeat Arjuna!" he thought, so he stood up and cried, "Wait, Acharya Drona! I have something to say." He then walked up to Karna and smilingly placed an arm around him. Karna was surprised.

Duryodhana turned to Drona and said, "What disqualifies this brave man from challenging Arjuna? Is it his lack of royalty? If so, then I have an announcement to make." Saying this, Duryodhana removed a silk cloth from his attire and slung it around Karna's shoulder. "Listen all of you present here," he said, "I hereby crown this young man as the King of Anga, the province that is under my rule. I have

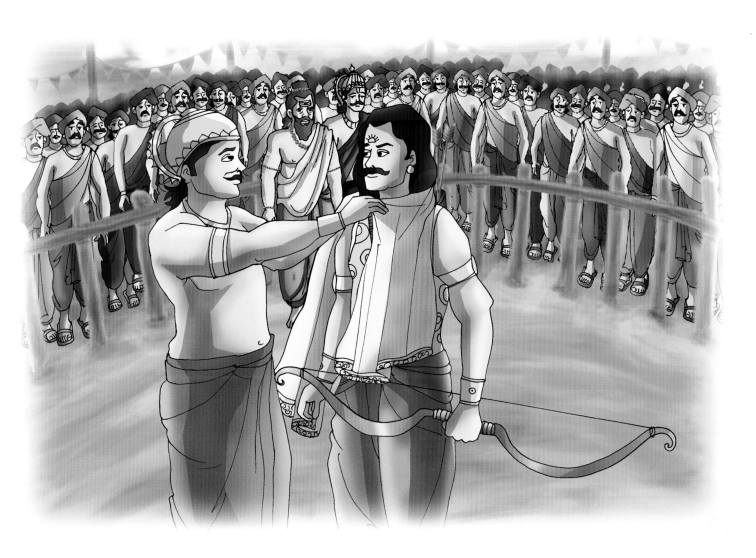

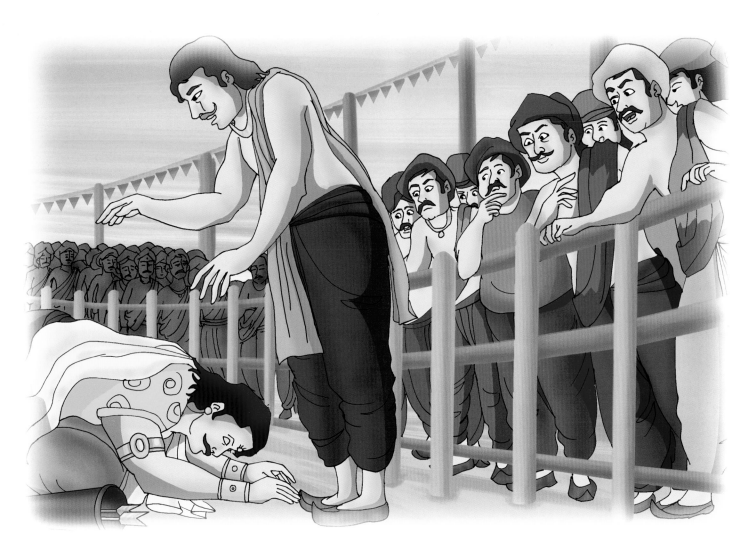

the right to nominate anyone I choose as the ruler of Anga, and so I have chosen this brave and skillful warrior. From now on, he shall be my best friend." He then smiled at Karna and said, "You are now qualified to fight Arjuna, O King of Anga!" Karna was filled with a deep sense of love and gratitude towards Duryodhana. "For this kind gesture, O friend," said Karna, "I shall ever be loyal to you. Come what may, this humble Karna shall always be at your side!"

As all this was happening, Adhiratha, Karna's foster father, entered the assembly. Karna bowed down and touched Adhiratha's feet. "Your son is now King, father!" said Karna. "Bless me!" "My blessings are always with you, son!" said Adhiratha.

As soon as the Pandavas heard this, they burst into laughter. "A charioteer's son?! Hahahahaha!"

Bheema mocked Karna. "A mere charioteer's son becomes King of Anga! What a joke! You are fit only for driving a chariot, young man, and not for ruling a province. Give up your dreams of competing with Arjuna! Hahahahaha!"

Karna felt humiliated, but could do nothing about it. Duryodhana once again came to his support. "Hold your tongue, Bheema," he shouted, "Karna may be a charioteer, but he has proved that he is a better warrior than any of you. I am sure he will prove to be a wise ruler as well." So saying, Duryodhana asked Karna and Adhiratha to board his chariot. The three then rode out of the ground. Meanwhile, Kunti had recognised Karna, seeing his golden armour and earrings. "He is my son," she thought, "the one I had abandoned years ago! What injustice that the son of Surya is being mocked at and I am in no position to call him my own?" The hapless mother couldn't bear the distress and fainted.

～ The Plot To Burn The Pandavas ～

As King Dhritarashtra grew old, he called a meeting with Bheeshma, Drona and Vidura. "I am now too old to rule!" said the King. "It's time to elect a new King. I have chosen my son, Duryodhana, to succeed me to the throne. What is the popular opinion?" Vidura replied, "Tradition stands witness that the eldest Prince shall succeed the King." Bheeshma and Drona supported Vidura's view. "That's right, O King!" they said, "Yudhishthira is elder to Duryodhana. So, as per tradition, he is the rightful heir to the throne."

Dhritarashtra agreed with the majority and elected Yudhishthira as his successor. But his decision did not go down well with Duryodhana. "How can father ignore me like that!" he grumbled. "I can't let Yudhishthira ascend the throne that rightfully belongs to me." He began to think of ways to get rid of the Pandavas.

Duryodhana went to meet Shakuni, his maternal uncle. "What troubles you, son?" asked Shakuni. "I want the throne, Uncle Shakuni," Duryodhana said, "but those five Pandava brothers are obstructing my path. Do something to get rid of them." "Don't worry, dear Duryodhana!" Shakuni said with a wicked smile, "At the first given opportunity, we will have the Pandavas killed. Then there won't be any obstacle between you and the throne of Hastinapur!"

In those days, a small town named Varnavata used to host a grand exhibition every year, and would invite the royal family to preside over the event. That year too, the people of Varnavata extended a cordial invitation to King Dhritarashtra and his family. Dhritarashtra requested Duryodhana to attend the exhibition on his behalf. Now Duryodhana and Shakuni wanted to make the best of this opportunity. They suggested to Dhritarashtra that he send the Pandavas to Varnavata.

"Let them represent the royal family, O father!" said Duryodhana. "And let them take their mother along," Shakuni added. "They will have a good time together." Dhritarashtra liked the idea and asked the Pandavas whether they would like to attend the exhibition. The Pandavas were glad to accept the proposal. The next morning they left for Varnavata.

Meanwhile, the people of Varnavata were busy with preparations for the exhibition. They needed to build a magnificent palace where the guests from Hastinapur could stay comfortably. For this they appointed a highly skilled contractor.

Now it so happened that the contractor who was entrusted with the job to construct the palace was a person known to Shakuni. "That makes my job easy!" Shakuni thought. He instantly hatched a wicked plan in his mind.

Shakuni bribed the contractor and asked him to use highly inflammable material like lac, resins, hemp, oil, and fat to build the palace for the Pandavas. "Don't worry, sire!" assured the corrupt contractor. "All will be done as per your command."

Shakuni then briefed Duryodhana with his plan. "I have appointed my men at Varnavata," he said. "They will set the palace on fire as soon as the Pandavas go to sleep at night. Hahaha!" Duryodhana was thrilled.

When the palace at Varnavata was ready, no one could detect that it was made up of inflammable material. The organizers instructed the guards to lead the royal guests into the palace when they arrive.

On the day of the exhibition, the five Pandava brothers and their mother, Kunti, arrived in Varnavata. They received a warm welcome and were invited to stay at the special palace, unaware of the danger in store for them.

But Vidura, through his spies, came to know of the plot to burn the Pandavas. He was always suspicious of the jealous Duryodhana and his evil-minded uncle Shakuni, so he had set spies on them. "Shakuni has planted men to burn the Pandavas alive in their palace and make it look like an accident," informed the spies. Vidura was a wellwisher of the Pandavas. He instantly sent his men to alert the Pandavas. He also instructed his men to dig a tunnel in the palace, so that the Pandavas could escape to safety before nightfall.

Vidura's men stealthily met the Pandavas and alerted them about the dangerous plot. Then they dug a tunnel that opened into the forest. That evening, the Pandavas along with Kunti, escaped through the tunnel. At midnight, according to the plan, the palace was set on fire. Soon, it was burnt to ashes. In the morning when the people saw this, they began to wail and cry at the accidental death of the Pandavas.

Duryodhana and Shakuni shook hands at the success of their plan. "Now I am at ease," sighed Duryodhana. "All my rivals are put to rest." "Celebrate, dear Duryodhana!" said Shakuni. "You are the undisputed King of Hastinapur."

Far away, in the middle of the forest, the Pandava brothers and Kunti were safe and secure. "We must thank Uncle Vidura!" said Yudhishthira. "It's because of him that we are alive today. Otherwise Duryodhana would surely have had us killed." "Let's go back to Hastinapur, brother!" Bheema cried, seething in anger, "I shall catch that Duryodhana by his throat and..."

"No, son!" Kunti interrupted him. "Let them think that we are dead. If we go back, they may try to kill us again. I won't allow you to risk your lives. Let's stay here for some time." The Pandavas agreed to stay in the forest, incognito. They built a small hut and lived there.

Bheema Weds Hidimbi

In the same forest, there lived a ferocious demon called Hidimba and his kind-hearted sister, Hidimbi. Hidimba liked to eat human flesh. As soon as he smelt the humans in the forest, his mouth started watering. "Hidimbi!" cried the demon, "There are humans around. Go find and kill them and bring them to me for breakfast. I am very hungry." Hidimbi did not like killing people, but she feared her cruel brother's wrath, so she went in search of the humans.

Wandering in search of them, Hidimbi came upon the Pandavas' hut. At that time, Bheema was guarding the hut while the others rested inside. As soon as Hidimbi saw the mighty human, she fell in love with him. She assumed the form of a beautiful maiden and approached Bheema. Bheema was surprised to see a lovely young maiden all alone in the dense forest.

"Who are you, O young lady?" he asked. "Aren't you afraid of roaming about alone?" Hidimbi came up to Bheema and said, "This forest is my home!"

In the meantime, Hidimba was feeling the pangs of hunger. "Where is Hidimbi?" he wondered. "Why hasn't she returned yet? Is she finding it too difficult to smell out and kill the humans?" More time passed, but Hidimbi still didn't return. Now Hidimba started to feel restless; he decided to go in search of his prey.

As Hidimba reached the Pandavas' hut, he saw Hidimbi, transformed into a beautiful woman, talking to Bheema. "I am in love with you, O mighty warrior," said Hidimbi to Bheema. "Will you marry me?"

Hidimba could not tolerate this. "HIDIMBI!" he roared. "What did I send you here for? Don't you know I am waiting for my food? Kill this human instantly!" Hidimbi was terribly frightened to see her cruel brother.

"What are you waiting for?" Hidimba cried again. "Kill him, I say."
"B...but brother..." Hidimbi said meekly. "I... can't!" Hidimba flew
into a rage. "I know why you can't kill him," cried Hidimba. "Because
you have fallen in love with him. How foolish of you! Now I shall kill
you both." Hidimba charged at Bheema. "Get ready to be killed,"
Hidimba roared. "Not that easy!" shouted Bheema, as he took on the
demon. It was a terrible duel. Bheema lifted Hidimba and banged
him on the ground. Hidimba sprang up and attacked Bheema again.
Both were mighty and skillful. Hidimba began to uproot trees and
hurl them at Bheema. In retaliation, Bheema lifted huge rocks and
threw them at Hidimba. Neither of them was ready to give up.

By now, hearing all the noise, Kunti and the other Pandava brothers
had gathered there. "Who is that terrible demon?" asked
Yudhishthira. "Why is he fighting with our Bheema?" wondered
Kunti. Finally, Bheema defeated the demon and killed him.

"I am proud of you, my son!" said Kunti. Then, she noticed Hidimbi standing aside. "Who is this beautiful woman?" asked Kunti. "And what was this fight all about?"

Hidimbi came forward, bowed before Kunti and revealed her real identity. She also disclosed how her cruel brother had wanted to kill Bheema. Then, Hidimbi confessed that she loved Bheema and wished to marry him. Kunti was pleased at Hidimbi's truthfulness. She realised that Hidimbi had sacrificed her own brother to save Bheema's life. "She truly loves Bheema!" thought Kunti.

"If you can, please accept me, mother..." Hidimbi said with tears in her eyes. "I surely will," replied Kunti, hugging Hidimbi with affection. She then turned to Bheema and said, "She deserves to be your wife, Bheema. Please marry her." Bheema agreed, but on the condition that he would leave Hidimbi after they have a child. Though it was an unusual condition, Hidimbi accepted it.

Bheema and Hidimbi were married. Yudhishthira and Kunti showered their blessings upon the couple while Arjuna, Nakula and Sahdeva gave them their best wishes.

Hidimbi was a good wife. She passed her days happily with Bheema. Soon they were blessed with a son. The child was healthy and strong. Bheema named him Ghatotkacha. Hidimbi's happiness knew no bounds, but at the same time she was also filled with worry and fear. As per Bheema's condition, she had to part with him after the birth of their child. "How will I live without you, my Lord?" she sighed, looking sadly at Bheema.

But, as she had already accepted the condition, she was ready to abide by it. "I shall raise our son in the best possible way," she said to Bheema, "and he will appear before you whenever you remember him!" Bheema then took leave of Hidimbi and Ghatotkacha. In time, Ghatotkacha was to become the most powerful and obedient son.

Bakasura Killed

Kunti and her sons now left the forest and entered Ekachakra, a city that lay on the outskirts of the forest. They decided to disguise themselves as Brahmins so that they would not be identified.

One day, a kind Brahmin woman saw them wandering about and invited them to her house. She gave them food and said, "Mine is a small family. You can stay with us as long as you wish." Kunti thanked her. The Pandavas began to live in the kind woman's house.

Every morning, the five brothers would go begging for alms. In the evening, they would return and call out to Kunti, "O mother, see what we have got today!" Kunti would say, "Whatever it is, share equally among yourselves, sons!" The obedient brothers would then share the alms they had collected. Days began to pass in this way.

One early morning, as soon as Kunti awoke, she was shocked to see the kind woman weeping. Kunti ran up to her and asked, "What is the matter, dear sister? Why are you crying? Is everything all right?" The woman went on crying without uttering a single word. Kunti sat beside her and consoled her. When the woman calmed down, she said, "My son is going to be eaten by the demon today."

Kunti was puzzled. The woman further explained, "On the outskirts of our city, there lives a giant demon called Bakasura. Everyday, he comes into the city and kills many people to eat. To stop this, the people promised him that they would send food for him every day. From that time, every morning, one person loads food on a bullock cart and takes it to the demon. The demon eats the food, the bullocks as well as the person who drives the cart. Today, my beloved son is supposed to take the cart to the demon. That is what breaks my heart!"

Kunti patiently heard everything, then said, "Don't lose heart, O sister! Your son shall not become the demon's food." "But that's not possible," said the woman. "If my son doesn't take food for Bakasura, he will come into the city and kill all of us."

"Nothing of that sort will happen," said Kunti. "Don't be afraid. In place of your son, my son, Bheema, will go to the demon; and I am sure this city will be freed from the demon forever."

"I can't let you sacrifice your son to save my son's life!" said the woman. But Kunti didn't listen and asked Bheema to drive the bullock cart, loaded with food, to the outskirts of the city where Bakasura lived. When Bakasura saw Bheema, he shouted, "Come fast! I am hungry."

Hearing this, Bheema stopped the bullocks, got off the cart and began to eat the food that was meant for the demon.

"Oh, you foolish human!" yelled Bakasura. "That food is meant for me. Don't you know that? How dare you eat it?" Bheema ignored the demon and continued to eat the food. At this, Bakasura became very angry. "You have invited death by eating my food. Now you get ready to become my food!" So shouting, he charged at Bheema; Bheema was alert, he swiftly turned around and pounced at Bakasura.

"You won't need food any more, you wicked demon!" cried Bheema. "I shall put an end to your life." In a terrible duel, mighty Bheema killed the ferocious demon.

He then drove the bullock cart back into the city. Seeing him return safe, Kunti was glad and the Brahmin woman heaved a sigh of relief. When the people of Ekachakra came to know all that had happened, they thanked Bheema and declared him 'the saviour of Ekachakra!'

Draupadi's Swayamvara

The Pandavas continued to live in the Brahmin woman's house. One fine morning, a sage visited them. He brought the news that King Drupada of Panchala was organising the swayamvara of his beautiful and brave daughter, Draupadi. "King Drupada has planned to hold a contest of archery. The best archer will be selected as the bridegroom," said the sage. The Pandavas were happy to hear this. "Let's go to the Kingdom of Panchala," suggested Bheema. "Our Arjuna must participate in this contest. He is the best archer." Yudhishthira, Nakula and Sahdeva too, were of the same opinion.

Early next morning, the five brothers left for the Kingdom of Panchala. On reaching, they were there, they were led into the swayamvara hall. Many revered Kings and Princes had arrived to take part in the contest. They all wished to win Draupadi's hand in marriage.

They were busy adjusting their royal crowns, or neatly folding their silk shawls. A few gave a last-minute brush to their robes, while others spruced up their looks. They all wanted to look their best.

The Pandavas were calm and composed, seated at the back. As they glanced at the gathering, they saw Duryodhana and Karna. "I knew they would come!" Bheema whispered to Arjuna. "Good that we are in the guise of Brahmins," said Arjuna. "No one will be able to recognise us."

The swayamvara hall had been beautifully painted. In the centre of the hall, there was a pillar upon which a huge revolving disc was fixed. From this disc hung a wooden fish. At the bottom of the pillar was another disc that was filled with water. A magnificent bow was placed on a table beside the pillar.

Draupadi had arrived in the hall and was seated next to her father, King Drupada. In her bridal attire, Draupadi looked stunningly beautiful. Her brother, Drishtidyumna was seated on the other side of the King. Another important invitee present in the hall was Lord Krishna, who Draupadi regarded as her brother.

When all the guests had arrived, King Drupada welcomed them and declared the contest open. "The participants will be given only one chance each," said Drishtidyumna. "Each participant has to lift the bow lying on that table and shoot an arrow into the fish's eye only by looking at its reflection in the water below. The one who succeeds shall be chosen as the bridegroom." The first participant came forward. He tried but could not even lift the bow. Then came the second but he too, failed to lift the bow. One after another, many aspiring Kings and Princes tried their luck, but in vain.

Now it was time for the King of Anga, Karna, to try his skills. As Karna got up from his seat, Duryodhana smiled at him and wished him luck. Karna smiled back at Duryodhana. He then bowed to King Drupada and the other distinguished guests and gracefully proceeded towards the table upon which the bow was placed. To everyone surprise, Karna lifted the bow effortlessly.

Krishna knew that the brave archer had the potential to hit the target. He exchanged glances with Draupadi for he knew that she wished to marry only Arjuna.

Krishna at once noticed the worry in Draupadi's eyes. He shook his head as if hinting to Draupadi that she should not allow Karna to participate in the contest. Draupadi understood Krishna's hint. She suddenly got up from her seat and said, "I have something to say to the gathering." Everyone was startled.

For a minute, there was complete silence in the hall. Then breaking the silence, Draupadi said, "I don't wish to marry a sutaputra*!"

Karna was taken aback, and so was the entire gathering. Duryodhana could not tolerate this insult of his dearest friend. "That's not fair, O proud Princess!" he fumed at Draupadi. "You have no right to humiliate my friend, the King of Anga!"

Draupadi replied, "He may be your friend. But his crown is just a favour from you. He has earned his Kingdom in charity. His true identity is that he is a sutaputra. This contest is open only to Kings and Princes who have royal blood running in their veins. Karna is disqualified."

There was nothing more to be said. Duryodhana and Karna could not take any more humiliation and walked out of the hall.

*Son of a charioteer

The contest resumed and many other participants came forward. But no one could even lift the bow, let alone shoot at the target. When almost all had given up, Bheema prompted Arjuna to take his turn. As Arjuna got up from his seat and slowly walked up to the centre of the hall, people watched him awestruck.

Some began to mock at him, "O clever Brahmin! One should praise your courage. You aspire to win Draupadi's hand! That too, when so many great archers have failed to do so. Hahaha!"

Undeterred by the remarks, Arjuna proceeded towards the bow. "Retreat, O Brahmin!" cried some Kings. But Krishna recognised the great archer. "There is my Arjuna!" he smiled in his heart.

Arjuna saluted the bow, gripped it firmly and picked it up in one go. Then he knelt down and aimed at the target, looking at its reflection.

King Drupada watched with surprise and confusion. He had always wished to make Arjuna his son-in-law. But who was this man? His costume suggested he was a Brahmin, but his gestures said he was an ace archer.

The entire gathering were kept guessing. "Will he make it?" wondered some. "He will only make a fool of himself. Hehehe!" laughed the others. Draupadi too, was puzzled. She looked at Krishna. There was a pleasant smile on Krishna's lips which was an assurance to the bride that the groom she wished to marry had arrived. "At last!" thought Draupadi, sighing in relief.

Meanwhile, Arjuna pulled his arrow and let it loose. It was right on target! "I knew it!" Krishna thought, nodding at Draupadi. Without any hesitation, Draupadi walked up to Arjuna and garlanded him.

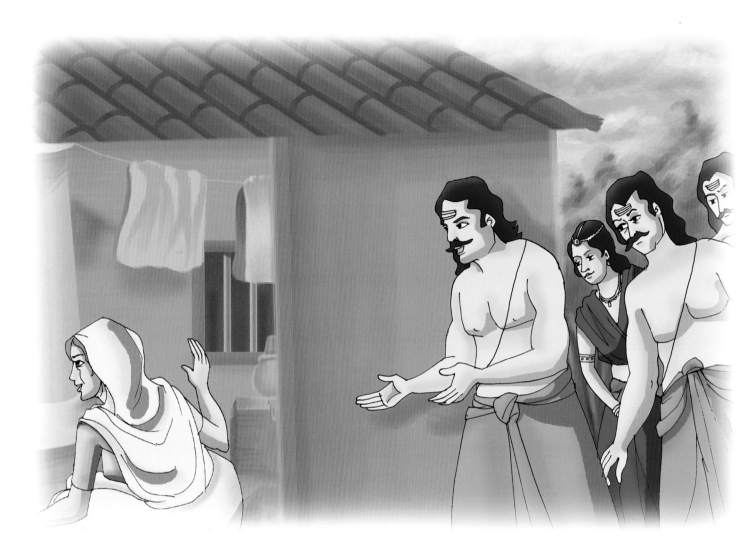

There were cheers all around for the Brahmin, but a handful of participants were of the view that a Brahmin was not eligible for the contest. "This victory should be nullified," they asserted, "as the contest was meant for those of the warrior caste only."

Krishna made good use of the commotion and helped the Pandavas and Draupadi escape to the city of Ekachakra. King Drupada wanted to know the real identity of the Brahmin who had won Draupadi. So he sent his son Drishtidyumna to follow Arjuna and Draupadi.

When the Pandavas reached home, they stood at the door and cried, "Where are you mother? See what we have brought today!" Kunti was busy with some household work. She thought her sons were talking about alms; she responded from inside, "Whatever it is, share it equally!"

Later, she saw the bride and realised the blunder she had committed. But her words were not to be taken back. As the five brothers had always obeyed their mother's command, this time too, they did the same. So Draupadi became the wife of all the five Pandava brothers.

Meanwhile, Drishtidyumna was glad to see that the Pandavas were alive and that Draupadi was married to none other than Arjuna – King Drupada's choice. He returned happily to his father and told him everything. King Drupada was overjoyed.

In a few days, Krishna and his elder brother, Balrama, went to Ekachakra to meet Kunti, who also happened to be their aunt. "We are happy to see you are all safe and secure, Aunt Kunti!" said Balrama. He and Krishna blessed the five brothers and Draupadi. They also promised Kunti that they would always help the Pandavas. Kunti hugged them with love and gratitude.

✑ The Kingdom of Indraprastha ✑

Meanwhile, the news spread that Kunti and her sons were alive and that Arjuna had won Draupadi's hand in marriage. The people were happy to know that their beloved Pandavas were safe. There were celebrations all around. Soon, the news reached Hastinapur. Duryodhana and Shakuni were shocked. "How is that possible?" Shakuni shouted, gritting his teeth. "My men had confirmed that the palace at Varnavata was burnt down to ashes; nothing was left. Then, how could the Pandavas have escaped? They have fooled us!"

Dhritarashtra and Gandhari were happy and called the Pandavas back to Hastinapur. On the King's summons, Kunti, her five sons, Draupadi and Krishna arrived in Hastinapur. Vidura, Bheeshma, Krishna and Dronacharya advised Dhritarashtra to honour the Pandavas by giving them their due share in the Kingdom.

In Vidura's opinion, the Pandavas had a stake over half the Kingdom. Bheeshma too, backed Vidura; but before taking the final decision, Dhritarashtra wanted to consult his dearest son, Duryodhana. When Duryodhana heard that the elders wanted to give half the Kingdom to the Pandavas, he seethed with anger. "How can they get half the Kingdom? Aren't we being too generous?" he shouted. Though Dhritarashtra too felt that ethically Pandavas deserved half the kingdom, he did not want to displease Duryodhana.

"We have to give them some land, son!" said Dhritarashtra. At first, Duryodhana refused to give them any land, but when the elders pressurized him, he agreed to give them Khandavaprastha, which was a deserted old city, now inhabited by fierce demons and wild beasts. "Let them go there and die," Duryodhana wished in his heart. "They don't deserve the comforts and luxuries of the royal palace."

Dhritarashtra called Yudhishthira and offered Khandavaprastha as their new Kingdom. Being humble and obedient, Yudhishthira accepted the land, though he was well aware of the fact that Khandavaprastha was a dense forest, not suitable inhabit. Agriculture was difficult and trade practices were almost impossible at Khandavaprastha. With all the religious rituals, Yudhishthira was crowned King of Khandavaprastha. Bheeshma and Dhritarashtra blessed the Pandavas.

The next day, the Pandavas left for Khandavaprastha. Krishna also went along with them. When they reached there, they could see nothing but huge trees, thorny bushes and poisonous creepers all around. "No one comes this way," said Bheema, "I've heard the land is infested with thieves and demons." "Don't worry, brother," said Yudhishthira, "We shall work hard to make this land worth living in."

Each of them were delegated a job. "We shall clear the forest," said Arjuna and Krishna. "Alright," said Bheema. "I shall remove the boulders! Let's start right away."

Arjuna and Krishna considered as to where to start the work. Suddenly, they heard a faint cry. As they turned around, they saw an old, weak man coming towards them. "Help! Help!" the man was crying in his feeble voice.

When he came close, Arjuna asked, "Who are you, O old man? And what are you doing here in this forest?" "I am Agni, the God of fire," replied the old man. "I am in distress, O great warriors! Indra, the King of Gods, is harassing me since I proved superior to him in a debate. He has not let me eat anything for a long time. I have lost all my strength. See how frail and weak I look! Now I have disguised myself and am trying to escape from him. Please help me!"

On saying this, Agni resumed his actual form. "Can we be of any help?" asked Arjuna, puzzled. Agni replied, "Only brave warriors like you two can help me. I want to eat this entire forest to satiate my hunger, but Indra will never let me do so. If you two can keep Indra at bay, I can eat freely." At this, Krishna said, "Fighting with Indra is no easy job. We need divine weapons to meet his prowess and skill." Agni closed his eyes for a moment and the next instant divine weapons appeared in his hands. He said to Arjuna, "This is Gandiva - an unbreakable bow. Please accept it from me." He also gave Arjuna two quivers that would always be full of arrows.

Then turning to Krishna, Agni said, "To you, O great one, I offer this Sudarshan Chakra* and this mace called Kaumodaki." Krishna and Arjuna thanked Agni for the weapons and went to block Indra's path as Agni spread his flames and began to eat the forest. He was so hungry that in no time he had consumed the entire forest.

*The Divine Discus

By the time Krishna and Arjuna returned, almost all the tall trees and thorny bushes had turned into ashes. The leftover shrubs and grasses were already in flames. Krishna and Arjuna were delighted that their job of clearing the forest was accomplished.

Just then, they heard someone crying for help. Turning around, they saw a demon running in fear. He was Mayasura, who had been living in the forest for a long time. Mayasura fell at Arjuna's feet and begged, "Agni has eaten up my home, O Arjuna, and now he wants to devour me too. Please protect me!"

"Arjuna," said Krishna, "it's your duty to help someone who has come to you seeking refuge. You must protect Mayasura's life." Arjuna made a humble request to Agni that he should let go of Mayasura. Agni spared the demon's life and returned to his abode. Mayasura heaved a huge sigh of relief and thanked Arjuna and Krishna.

"I want to repay your kindness, O Arjuna!" said Mayasura. "I am blessed with divine architectural powers. Please allow me to build a palace for you all." Arjuna happily agreed. Mayasura then invoked his celestial powers and began to erect a magnificent palace for the Pandavas. Plant and animal life began to prosper in the surrounding area.

When the palace was complete, it looked truly amazing. The Pandavas thanked Mayasura and gave him a warm farewell. "Let us rename this place, Indraprastha!" said Krishna. The Pandavas liked the idea and Khandavaprastha came to be known as Indraprastha. Yudhishthira declared it his capital city. The righteous Pandavas and their Indraprastha received blessings from the Gods and Angels. People who loved and respected the Pandavas migrated from Hastinapur and settled down in Indraprastha. It was also frequented by the saints. Soon, Indraprastha was as glorious a Kingdom as Hastinapur.

Seeing that the Pandavas were well settled in their Kingdom, Krishna decided to take leave. "I have to look after my Kingdom now," he said to the Pandavas, "but I shall come to you whenever you want any help." He then left for his Kingdom, Dwarka.

Yudhishthira proved to be a wise and generous ruler. Many neighbourhood Kings extended their hands of friendship towards him. The weaker ones merged their Kingdoms with Indraprastha and accepted Yudhishthira's sovereignty. Due to the Pandavas' amicable attitude, all their allies pledged unflinching support to them.

Indraprastha soon became the most powerful Kingdom and Yudhishthira the most influential King. Krishna often visited the Pandavas to guide them on various issues. Of all the five Pandava brothers, Arjuna was the closest to Krishna. Together, they shared the bond of friendship as well as that of a teacher and disciple.

∽ Arjuna Weds Subhadra ∽

Krishna had a younger sister named Subhadra. She was very beautiful and talented. One day, as she was going to a temple, she happened to see a handsome young man and fell in love with him. The young man was none other than Arjuna, who was on a visit to Dwarka. Arjuna too fell in love with Subhadra. Both of them opened their hearts to each other and vowed to marry.

Krishna somehow came to know about their love and his heart was filled with happiness. "Brave Arjuna is the best choice for my dear sister!" he thought. Meanwhile, not knowing any of this, Balrama had arranged Subhadra's marriage to Duryodhana. One day, Balrama went up to Krishna and said, "The time has come to get our sister married." "That's right, brother!" Krishna nodded. Balrama further added, "I have chosen Duryodhana for Subhadra."

Krishna was shocked to hear this. He could not approve of Balrama's choice, but it was not the right time to open an argument since Balrama had already taken the decision; so Krishna kept quiet.

That night, he pondered over it. "Duryodhana is so wicked and crafty, Subhadra can never be happy with him." But it was almost impossible to make Balrama change his decision. "I will have to think of some other way to unite Arjuna and Subhadra," Krishna decided. The next day, he went to Subhadra and told her about Balrama arranging her marriage with Duryodhana. Subhadra was shocked and saddened. She had already given her heart to Arjuna. How could she accept someone else as her husband? "Elope with Arjuna!" suggested Krishna. "Perhaps this is the only option we are left with." "But... brother!" Subhadra said. "How can we go against brother Balrama?" "Don't worry, sister!" said Krishna. "By no means are we going against him. Instead, we are stopping him from making a blunder. Duryodhana is not fit to be your husband."

Following Krishna's advice, Arjuna and Subhadra eloped from Dwarka and got married. Soon the news reached Balrama's ears. "How dare she elope?" Balrama shouted, mad with shock and anger. "I never thought my sister would bring disgrace to us!"

"Your anger is natural, brother Balrama!" said Krishna. "But think again. Hasn't Subhadra saved us from a greater disgrace?" "What do you mean?" Balrama yelled. "Speak clearly, Krishna! Don't talk in riddles at this time." Krishna explained, "Duryodhana is a greater disgrace, O brother. He is overambitious and greedy. He will go to any extent to fulfil his selfish motives. By marrying off Subhadra to Duryodhana, we would have pushed our beloved sister into a valley of suffering and sadness. Moreover, Subhadra had already selected Arjuna as her life partner. She wouldn't have lived happily with anyone else." Balrama realised that Arjuna was a superior choice. He forgave Subhadra and heartily accepted Arjuna as his brother-in-law.

The couple received blessings from Krishna and Balrama and returned to Indraprastha. Arjuna and Subhadra were happy together. Soon, Subhadra was expecting a child. One night, she was restless. "I am not able to sleep, dear!" she said to Arjuna. To amuse her, Arjuna began to tell her stories of wars and battles. This was Subhadra's favourite topic. She listened with interest and zeal. Then she asked, "What is Chakravyuha? I have heard it's the most tricky battle formation. Please tell me more about it!"

Arjuna began to explain, "Chakravyuha is a seven-tier spiral formation of the army. The soldiers are arranged in seven layers, and their leader stands inside the innermost layer. Indeed, it's the most tricky battle formation. Anyone who wants to enter the Chakravyuha has to penetrate the seven layers one by one. After killing the enemy, he again needs to penetrate the seven layers to come out." As Arjuna spoke, Subhadra listened sleepily; so did the child in her womb.

"Very few warriors know how to penetrate the layers of the Chakravyuha," Arjuna described. "First layer is broken like this... and then the warrior has to fight the soldiers arranged in the second layer. After penetrating the second layer, his path is blocked by the soldiers of the third layer. One can penetrate the third layer this way..."

Gradually, Arjuna explained the method to penetrate all the seven layers. By now Subhadra's eyelids were heavy with sleep. Just as Arjuna began to describe how to come out of the Chakravyuha, Subhadra fell asleep. So, she as well as her child, did not hear the full narration.

Some days later, Subhadra gave birth to a beautiful baby boy. The child was named 'Abhimanyu', meaning one who always defends his honour. The child was a source of pride and joy for his father and uncles. They taught him all the religious scripts as well as different forms of warfare.

Jarasandha And Shishupala Slain

Indraprastha was flourishing. Days were happy and nights peaceful. One day, Sage Narada happened to visit Yudhishthira's court. Yudhishthira himself went out to welcome the revered sage. The other Pandava brothers arranged for Narada's comfortable stay at the palace.

After some time, Narada sat for a chat with Yudhishthira. "I have a suggestion to make, King Yudhishthira!" he said. "Please, go ahead and tell me!" said Yudhishthira. "Indraprastha is now a glorious Kingdom," said Narada. "Your able administration has led you far ahead of almost all of your contemporaries. In my opinion, you should perform the Rajasuya Yagna*, but beware of the other jealous and crafty Kings, who may try to ruin your yagna." Narada's suggestion appealed to Yudhishthira, but before taking a final decision, he wanted to consult Krishna. So, after Narada left, Yudhishthira invited Krishna for a discussion.

*A sacred sacrifice performed by a King to declare his superiority over other Kings

Krishna soon arrived. Yudhishthira told him what Sage Narada had advised. "I need your guidance on the matter, O Krishna!" said Yudhishthira. "Should I perform the Rajasuya Yagna?"

"Why not?" said Krishna, with a smile. "You have all the qualities to become an Emperor, dear Yudhishthira! It's time you declare yourself the sovereign, the King of Kings. Performing the Rajasuya Yagna is a noble thought. I shall support you in all the ways I can."

At the same time, Krishna warned Yudhishthira. "Before you start making preparations for the yagna," he said, "I must tell you that there is a King who might put obstacles in your way."

"Who is he?" asked Yudhishthira. Krishna replied, "Jarasandha, the mighty King of Magadha!" "But why would he try to obstruct my way, O Krishna?" asked Yudhishthira, puzzled.

Krishna said, "Jarasandha is overambitious. He has already declared himself an Emperor. In the past he has attacked and defeated many Kings. Some of them chose to flee from their Kingdoms to save their lives. Jarasandha has but one desire, to become the mightiest of all. He has captured many Kings with the motive to sacrifice them at the altar of Lord Rudra. If he succeeds in his motive, he shall become invincible."

"What do we do then?" asked Yudhishthira, a little worried. "Shall I drop the idea of a yagna?" Krishna thought for a while then said, "It's true that we can't defeat Jarasandha by force. But we can remove him from our way by tricking him." Krishna then called Bheema and told him about Jarasandha. "I will tell you Jarasandha's weak point," said Krishna, "and you can destroy him!" Bheema agreed. Krishna began to narrate, "Jarasandha's father had two wives but no children..."

Bheema listened carefully. Krishna continued, "One day, a saint visited Jarasandha's father. When he came to know that Jarasandha's father wished for a son, he gave him a mango. "Give this mango to your Queen and she will be a mother soon," said the sage. Jarasandha's father divided the mango into two equal pieces and gave one piece each to both his wives. By the sage's blessings, both the queens became pregnant. But, at the time of delivery, to their shock and fear, they both gave birth to half a baby boy. Thinking it to be a bane, they had the half-babies thrown into the forest. Just then, a demoness called Jara happened to pass through the same forest. When she saw the half-babies, she was filled with curiosity. She picked them up and placed them side by side. Instantly, there was a miracle; the two halves joined together and the baby boy came to life."

"Hmm! And that is Jarasandha right?" Bheema asked. "That's right!" said Krishna. "There is only one way to destroy Jarasandha."

"What is that?" asked Bheema. "If the two halves of his body are ripped apart, he will die," replied Krishna, "and only you are capable of doing that, Bheema!"

Bheema agreed to fight Jarasandha. When Yudhishthira came to know of this, he was worried and said, "How can I send my beloved brother into the cruel hands of Jarasandha?" "Don't worry, dear Yudhishthira," Krishna assured. "I shall take care of Bheema." Finally Yudhishthira gave his consent.

It was decided that Krishna, Arjuna and Bheema would disguise themselves as Brahmins, so that they could enter Jarasandha's court. So, as per plan, they went to the Kingdom of Magadha. At first, Jarasandha took them to be Brahmins and welcomed them. But when he saw the scars and wounds on Bheema's bare body, he had a doubt. "They seem to be warriors!" he thought.

When Krishna saw Jarasandha in a pensive mood, he instantly understood what was going on in Jarasandha's mind. "What are you thinking, O great King?" asked Krishna. "I doubt you are Brahmins!" Jarasandha replied. "You are right," pat came Krishna's reply. "Actually, we are warriors and have come here to challenge you to a duel!"

Arjuna, Bheema and Krishna then introduced themselves. "I have heard that you have held many Kings captive," said Bheema. "If you don't wish to invite my wrath, then release those captives." "Hahaha!" Jarasandha laughed. "What if I don't release them?" "Then get ready to be killed by me!" said Bheema. At this, Jarasandha flew into a rage and attacked Bheema. Krishna and Arjuna smiled to themselves, as everything was going according to their plan. Jarasandha and Bheema wrestled with each other. The duel continued for thirteen days. But neither of them was ready to accept defeat.

Krishna noticed that Jarasandha was getting exhausted. He picked up a straw and waited for Bheema to look at him. Bheema too was feeling tired and confused. He glanced at Krishna, as if asking him how to defeat Jarasandha.

Krishna made good this opportunity and indicated to Bheema that he should look at the straw in his hand. As Bheema lowered his eyes to the straw, Krishna split the straw into two pieces. Bheema instantly understood that Krishna was asking him to rip apart the two halves of Jarasandha's body. He caught Jarasandha by his legs, tore him into two halves and threw them away.

Surprisingly, the two halves of Jarasandha's body once again joined together and he came back to life. Bheema was puzzled. He again looked at Krishna. Now Krishna took another straw, tore it into two halves, but this time threw the left half to the right and the right half to the left.

Taking the cue from Krishna, Bheema tore Jarasandha's body into two halves again. Then he threw the right half to the left and the left half to the right, just as Krishna had done with the straw.

This time, Jarasandha's body did not join together and he was destroyed forever. Krishna and Arjuna hugged and praised Bheema. "Only you could do it, Bheema!" said Krishna. "Thank you, for having faith in me!" said Bheema.

Then, they removed their disguise and reverted back to their original selves. "First, let's release all the captive Kings," said Krishna. They hurried towards the dungeon where Jarasandha had kept his captives. Krishna, Arjuna and Bheema freed the Kings. "We are grateful to you!" cried the Kings in unison. They promised to participate in Yudhishthira's imperial Yagna. After this, Krishna, Bheema and Arjuna returned to Indraprastha.

Meanwhile in Indraprastha, preparations for the yagna were in full swing. Nakula and Sahdeva had sent invitations to the Kings and sages far and wide. Yudhishthira had sent special messengers to Hastinapur to invite King Dhritarashtra and all the other members of the royal family. Bheeshma, Drona, Vidura and Dhritarashtra were happy to accept the invitation. Bheeshma blessed Yudhishthira in his heart. "I am proud of you, Yudhishthira!" he thought. "I knew you would be Emperor one day."

The royal delegation, comprising Dhritarashtra, Bheeshma, Drona, Vidura, Kripacharya and all the Kaurava Princes soon arrived in Indraprastha. On the stipulated day and time, Sage Vyasa kindled the sacrificial fire. Amidst the chanting of sacred verses, Yudhishthira performed the yagna. At the completion of the yagna, Yudhishthira was proclaimed Emperor!

All the Kings and rulers present at the occasion accepted Yudhishthira's superiority and sovereignty. Sage Vyasa then addressed Yudhishthira, "It is customary for the Emperor to select the best among Kings. Please perform the ritual!"

Yudhishthira requested Bheeshma and other elders to perform the ritual on his behalf and select the best among Kings. Bheeshma suggested Krishna's name. "Krishna is powerful, compassionate, wise and experienced," said Bheeshma. "He is undoubtedly the best among Kings." Drona and Vidura lauded Bheeshma's choice. Just then, a voice was heard from the gathering, "Krishna doesn't deserve the title." Every head turned towards the voice, which was that of Shishupala, the wicked Prince of Chedi. Shishupala also happened to be Krishna's cousin. "Someone as selfish and deceitful as Krishna can't be chosen for this title," Shishupala cried.

Hearing this, Bheema sprang up and shouted, "Mind your language, Shishupala. An insult to Krishna's name is an insult to our name. We won't take it." But Krishna stopped him. "Let him speak, Bheema!" said Krishna. "Hah! No one dare stop me!" Shishupala said in a vain tone. "I will speak the truth. This Krishna is good for nothing." "Behave yourself, Shishupala!" shouted Arjuna. "You don't have any right to humiliate Krishna! Our Krishna is the best!" "O really?" mocked Shishupala. "You are under a grave delusion. Krishna is crafty and cunning. He has cheated all of you. In reality, he is a mere cowherd."

Suddenly, Krishna shouted, "Enough, Shishupala! That was your hundredth mistake. Now if you make another mistake, I won't spare you!" The entire gathering was stunned to hear Krishna's words. "You don't know who you are and your past!" Krishna explained. "When you were born, Shishupala, you had four arms and a third eye on the forehead."

Shishupala's eyes opened wide as he listened to Krishna's narration. "We were shocked to see a baby with four arms and three eyes," Krishna continued. "Just then we heard a divine voice that said, 'The baby boy will soon lose his two extra arms and the third eye. He shall be a normal child. But he will be killed by the one on whose lap he loses his two arms and the third eye.' We all could not believe our ears."

Even Shishupala could not believe what he had heard. Krishna continued his narration: "People present there began to cuddle you and shower their blessings on you. Many relatives took you on their laps but nothing unusual happened. Then your mother placed you in my lap. Suddenly, your two extra arms and the third eye disappeared. Though your mother was happy that you became a normal child, she also was worried that you would be killed by me, according to the prophesy. She began to wail and beg that I must spare your life, so I made a promise to her." Krishna stopped here.

"What promise?" asked Shishupala. Krishna replied, "I promised that I will overlook your mistakes a hundred times. Since then, I have been excusing your sins. Today, you have reached that hundredth mark. Now just one more mistake and you will meet your end."

"Hahaha! Don't tell me stories!" Shishupala laughed arrogantly. "A foolish cowherd is warning me?"

"Be careful, Shishupala!" Krishna cried. "You have crossed your limit!" So saying, Krishna flung his Sudarshan Chakra at Shishupala and slew him. The evil Shishupala met his deserved end. After performing its task, the Sudarshan Chakra returned to Krishna's finger. Due to the impact of the Chakra's rotation, Krishna's finger began to bleed. Draupadi, who was all the while observing what was happening between Krishna and Shishupala, instantly noticed this and ran to Krishna. She tore off a corner of her veil and bandaged Krishna's wound. Krishna smiled and said, "Some day, O sister, I shall repay the debt of each thread of your veil."

∽ The Game Of Dice ∽

Krishna was unanimously declared the best of all Kings. All the dignitaries praised and honoured him. Yudhishthira had arranged for a grand feast. The guests had a good time in Indraprastha. Yudhishthira then honoured them with precious gifts. With all the rituals complete, Dhritarashtra and the other delegates from Hastinapur also wanted to leave. Yudhishthira, his four brothers and Draupadi touched the elders' feet and took their blessings. "May you always usher in peace and prosperity, my children!" said Grandsire Bheeshma, with moist eyes.

They all left for Hastinapur. But Duryodhana stayed back, as he wished to spend some time in Indraprastha. He was amazed at the fine architecture of the royal palace. The great assembly hall was designed by Mayasura with a lot of illusionary effects. At one place, Duryodhana thought it was a passage. But it was only a wall and Duryodhana bumped into it.

Just then, he heard loud laughter. Duryodhana turned around angrily and saw Draupadi standing in the gallery, laughing at him. Duryodhana was embarrassed but pretended to be unaffected by Draupadi's laughter.

As he walked on, he noticed water under his feet. So, he began to walk carefully, trying to avoid the water and place his feet only on the dry floor. "Hahahahahaha!" Draupadi laughed again. "It isn't water, it is only an illusion, Prince Duryodhana! You need not walk that carefully!"

Duryodhana again had to hide his embarrassment and anger. Hardly had he walked two steps when he came across another illusion. The floor looked like dry ground but actually there was a shallow pool of water in the centre of the hall. Obviously he could not see the pool and fell into it. This time Draupadi's laughter was very loud. "HAHAHAHAHAHA! Blind son of a blind father!" she mocked at Duryodhana.

Draupadi's laughter infuriated Duryodhana. "Hold your tongue, you proud woman!" he shouted at Draupadi. "One day you will have to pay for this laughter!"

That very moment, in his heart, Duryodhana swore revenge. He then left Indraprastha and returned to Hastinapur. After that, he remained restless. "I will destroy the Pandavas," he would seethe every now and then.

His uncle, Shakuni noticed his restlessness and came to comfort him. "What disturbs you, son?" Shakuni asked. "What is it that you long for?" "Revenge... Uncle Shakuni! REVENGE!" Duryodhana responded angrily. "I can't rest easy till I put those Pandavas to death." "We will, dear Duryodhana!" Shakuni said, patting Duryodhana's shoulder. "Let's make a plan to annihilate the Pandavas." They began to work on a conspiracy.

Shakuni advised Duryodhana to be diplomatic. "Be calm, Duryodhana!" he said. "Your enemies should not know that you are angry with them and are seeking revenge." After thinking for a while, Shakuni came up with an idea. "Invite Yudhishthira to a friendly game of dice!" he said. At first, Duryodhana didn't like the idea. "I want to ruin them completely, Uncle Shakuni!" he said. "How will a game of dice help?" "It will, son!" Shakuni, who was an expert at the game of dice, assured him. "Let me toss the dice for you. I promise you, I will beat them in every bet, until they lose their entire Kingdom to us."

Now the plan was clear to Duryodhana and he agreed to it. "Great, Uncle Shakuni!" he cried in joy. "I shall send an invitation to the Pandavas. Let them come here!" "Only to be wiped out," Shakuni added. They both shared an evil laugh. The next day Duryodhana sent his messenger to Indraprastha, inviting Yudhishthira and his brothers to Hastinapur for a friendly game of dice.

Acknowledging the invitation, Yudhishthira, Bheema, Arjuna, Nakula, Sahdeva and Draupadi left for Hastinapur. The game was to be held in the large assembly hall. The gallery was arranged and decorated. When the Pandavas arrived in Hastinapur, they received a warm welcome. Yudhishthira and his brothers were led into the assembly hall, while Draupadi was taken to meet the Queen and other Princesses.

Dhritarashtra, Bheeshma, Acharya Drona, Vidura, Kripacharya, and others were seated in the gallery. The dice board was set up in the centre of the hall. On one side sat Duryodhana, Shakuni, and Dushasana while on the other side sat Yudhisthira and his four brothers. Duryodhana declared that Shakuni would toss the dice for the Kauravas. Yudhisthira agreed and the game began. Initially, a small amount of money and jewelry were wagered from both sides. Shakuni rolled the dice and won the toss. Duryodhana was delighted.

As the game progressed, Yudhishthira went on losing his wealth. Every time, Shakuni would toss the dice in such a way that the Kauravas would win the bet. Yudhishthira was bound to lose as the game was already unequal because of Shakuni's magical dice. Having lost all his wealth, Yudhishthira staked his Kingdom, Indraprastha.

"Hahahahaha!" Shakuni laughed. "We have won THIS bet too, Duryodhana!" "This is wonderful, Uncle Shakuni! But it comes as no surprise to me. I knew Yudhishthira would lose every bet! Indraprastha – the glorious Kingdom – now belongs to me!" Duryodhana said, excitedly slapping his thighs.

As Yudhishthira watched in dismay, Duryodhana mocked him, "Hah! There sits a King without a Kingdom! Your crown has no meaning now! Why don't you take it off?" A dejected Yudhishthira removed his crown and placed it near the dice board.

"Now, what have you got to stake next, brother?" Duryodhana asked, with a wicked smile. Seeing Yudhishthira unable to speak, Shakuni provoked him, "So what if you have lost your entire wealth and Kingdom! You still have four mighty brothers. Stake them and take a chance." Yudhishthira, a losing gambler, had lost all reason and common sense. In the hope of winning back his Kingdom, he staked Bheema, but lost again! Then one by one, he staked and lost Arjuna, Nakula and Sahdeva, too.

"Don't lose heart, Yudhishthira!" Shakuni again provoked him, "You can stake yourself and win back everything." Yudhishthira staked himself and lost. "You five brothers are our slaves now!" shouted Dushasana. "You will have to do as we say. You should not wear a crown as it is not meant to be worn by slaves." Bheema, Arjuna, Nakula and Sahdeva removed their crowns and placed them on the floor. Yudhishthira knew Shakuni was cheating, but he was as helpless as the mute spectators sitting in the gallery.

"Yudhishthira, you don't have anything more that you can stake!" mocked Duryodhana. "It is better you quit this game and surrender to me. I shall allow you to lead a life of an ordinary man in Hastinapur."

These humiliating words, instead of dissuading Yudhishthira, further stimulated him to play and try to regain the lost Kingdom. As the saying goes, "hope never dies in a gambler", Yudhishthira asked Shakuni to continue the game. "But what would you bet?" asked Dushasana. Yudhishthira was in a fix. Suddenly, Shakuni intervened, "Yudhishthira! You have one last chance! Stake Draupadi and win back all that you have lost." By this time Yudhishthira was really desperate. He fell prey to Shakuni's provocation, and staked Draupadi as his final bet.

But as fate would have it, Yudhishthira lost this bet too. The courtiers standing outside the gallery were stunned. "How shameful!" they said. "They have ruined their glorious past."

"Hahaha!" Duryodhana laughed, "Now Draupadi too, belongs to us!" He ordered his younger brother, Dushasana, "Go and bring Draupadi here, she is also our slave now!" Hearing this, the Pandavas flew into a rage. Bheema and Arjuna charged at Dushasana. But Duryodhana stopped them. "Have you forgotten that you are all our slaves to us?" said Duryodhana. "Slaves don't have any right to interfere with what their masters do."

Dushasana went to Draupadi's chamber and said, "Come with me! You are now a slave. Yudhishthira has lost you in the game of dice." Draupadi was furious. "Hold your tongue, Dushasana!" she shouted. "I am your elder brother's wife. You should never talk to me like this." At this, Dushasana grabbed Draupadi's hair and shouted, "You slave! How dare you disobey me?" Then he dragged Draupadi into the court, holding her by her hair. "Here she is, brother Duryodhana!" cried Dushasana. The entire court watched in shocked silence.

Draupadi was aghast. She looked at her husbands. "Why are all of you sitting quiet? Your wife is being humiliated. Won't you intervene?" "They can't!" mocked Duryodhana. "They have lost themselves as well. Your five mighty husbands too, are my slaves."

Draupadi now turned to the gallery and pleaded to the elders, "O wise men, will you just be mute spectators to this grave injustice being done to me? I have a question to ask. Is there no rule in this game? How can Yudhishthira stake me when he himself had become a slave? Tell me... HOW?"

No one had any reply. King Dhritarashtra sat with his head bowed in shame. "Oh, this should never have happened! But who can stop Duryodhana? Not even I. I wish I had died before witnessing all this," he thought. Drona, Bheeshma, Vidura and all the others were feeling the same helpless frustration.

Suddenly, Duryodhana cried, "Draupadi, you are a slave. You should not be dressed like a Queen. I command you to take off your royal robes." At this, Bheeshma arose from his seat and shouted, "Enough, Duryodhana! Stop this immoral and unethical act. It will only lead to your downfall, and we all shall pay for your misdeeds."

"Nothing is immoral or unethical, Grandsire!" Duryodhana yelled back. "Yudhishthira is mature enough to understand the rules of the game. He himself chose to stake his wife. What can I do if he lost the bet? Now that Draupadi is my slave, nothing I do is immoral or unethical."

Duryodhana then prompted Dushasana to disrobe Draupadi. "Right away, brother!" responded Dushasana readily. He grabbed Draupadi's veil and began to pull it off. "Leave me alone!" Draupadi cried, "Let go of my veil." She then appealed to everyone, "Someone please save my honour!" But no one dared to come to her rescue.

Draupadi was helpless. She closed her eyes and began to chant Krishna's name. "Save me, Lord!" she prayed. "I have no one but you. Please help me in this hour of peril." Wicked Dushasana went on removing Draupadi's veil, while Draupadi kept chanting Krishna's name.

To everyone's awe and surprise, there seemed to be no end to Draupadi's veil. It was a miracle! Dushasana went on pulling it but couldn't disrobe Draupadi as her veil seemed endless. Completely exhausted with the effort, he collapsed. Draupadi and the Pandavas heaved a huge sigh of relief. "Your magic has protected my modesty, O Lord!" Draupadi said in her heart, thanking Krishna. "I shall be ever indebted to you." Krishna replied to her, "You need not be grateful, dear Draupadi. I have not done any favour to you. I have only returned a debt. At one time you dressed my wound with your veil and I had promised to return the debt of each thread. That's why I did it. I shall always be there for you, sister!"

Draupadi then clutched her disheveled hair and took a vow. "I will not tie up my hair until I have it washed in Dushasana's blood," she proclaimed. Bheema too, took a vow. "I will hack off Dushasana's sinful hands with which he has touched Draupadi's veil. Until I bring Dushasana's blood to wash Draupadi's hair, I swear, I won't rest."

Duryodhana was disappointed that Dushasana couldn't disrobe Draupadi. Out of vengeance, he yelled, "Come, sit on my lap, Draupadi! Your master commands you. OBEY, you slave!" At this, Bheema shouted, "You will pay for this, Duryodhana. I vow to break your thigh and drink your blood."

All this while, Dhritarashtra had been quiet. Now he spoke, "Enough, Duryodhana! How long will you carry on this ugly game?" He then addressed Draupadi, "O chaste daughter! I am ashamed of my sons' behaviour. I free you from slavery. Forgive me if you can, and ask for a boon!"

Draupadi asked that Yudhishthira be freed from slavery. Dhritarashtra granted the boon and said, "Ask for another boon, and it will be yours." Draupadi asked that Bheema, Arjuna, Nakula and Sahdeva too, be freed from slavery. Dhritarashtra granted this wish as well and requested Draupadi to ask for one more. At this, Draupadi replied, "Nothing more than the freedom of my husbands I desire, Grandsire."

Dhritarashtra then addressed Yudhishthira, "I know my sons have taken away your Kingdom by trickery. Hence, I return it to you, O Yudhishthira." The Pandavas returned to their Kingdom.

Duryodhana, however, could not digest Dhritarashtra's generosity. That night, he went to his father's chamber and said, "Think practically, O father! We have insulted the Pandavas. If they are allowed to stay in Indraprastha, they will surely attack and kill us." Dhritarashtra was convinced. "What do we do then?" he asked.

Duryodhana responded, "Before they annihilate us, we should drive them out of their Kingdom!" "But how is that possible?" asked Dhritarashtra. "Allow me to invite them for another game of dice," said Duryodhana. "We will defeat them once again. This time, the loser shall be exiled for thirteen years."

Dhritarashtra gave his consent and the Pandavas were invited one more time. A new game of dice was to be played between the Kauravas and Pandavas. "The rules are different this time," said Duryodhana. "The one who loses will have to give up all his belongings and go into the forest. He will have to live in exile for twelve years, and thereafter one year in disguise. During the last year, if the loser is identified by anyone, he will be forced to live another twelve years in exile and one more year incognito." The Pandavas agreed to the rules and the game started. Shakuni's wicked tricks worked once again and the Pandavas were defeated. Duryodhana was happy that his plan had worked well.

≈ The Exile Begins ≈

The Pandava brothers gave up their royal robes and put on simple clothes like ascetics. Draupadi also wished to accompany her husbands to the forest. When Kunti saw her children's plight, she fainted with shock and sorrow. She was then shifted to Vidura's house where she would stay till her sons returned from exile.

As the Pandavas left, Bheeshma watched them go. Blessing them in his heart, the Grandsire broke into tears. "I couldn't do anything for you, my children," Bheeshma uttered. "Let God be your saviour! Live in peace, wherever you may be!" Some people of Indraprastha, a few Brahmins and Yudhishthira's chief priest, Sage Dhaumya, also followed the Pandavas into the forest. They walked until they reached the banks of the river Ganga. It was late evening by then, so they decided to halt there for the night. Yudhishthira requested the people who followed them to return to Indraprastha, but they refused.

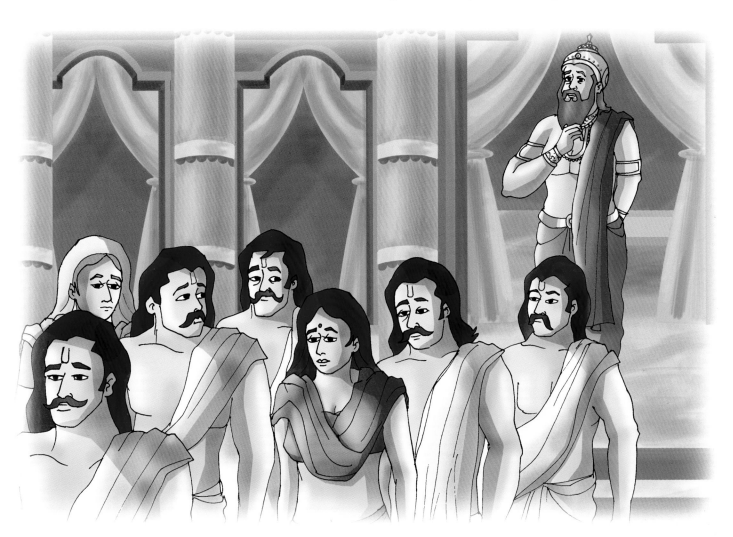

That night as Yudhishthira slept, Sage Vyasa appeared in his dreams and taught him a sacred chant. "Pray to Surya, the Sun God, and chant this verse a hundred and one times," he said. Yudhishthira awoke with a start. Before dawn, he walked to the river and waited for the sunrise. Just at dawn, Yudhishthira waded into the holy Ganga and worshipped Surya, chanting the verse that Sage Vyasa had taught him.

Pleased by his worship, Surya appeared before him. He was carrying a vessel in his hand. "Take this divine vessel, Yudhishthira!" said Surya. "Use it for your daily food. Let it be in Draupadi's custody. The vessel will be filled with an unlimited quantity of the food you desire each day. It will not be empty until Draupadi finishes her meal. However, it will be filled only once a day." Yudhishthira accepted the vessel from Surya and thanked him. He asked Sage Dhaumya and the others to return to their respective homes, as the exile was meant only for the Pandavas. Thereafter, the Pandavas crossed the Ganga and entered the forest.

They settled down in a clearing that looked relatively free from wild animals and demons. When the news of their exile reached Krishna, he instantly came to the forest to meet his beloved Pandavas and Draupadi.

"It's sad to see you live like this," said Krishna with a heavy heart. "But don't lose heart; times will change. Be vigilant! The ordeal you are facing today is for your good, as experience is the only source of knowledge. Your hardships will only make you wiser and cleverer. Prepare yourselves to achieve higher goals in life."

Soon, Sage Vyasa too paid a visit to the Pandavas. He advised them to spend their days in increasing their power and talents. "You will need immense power to regain your Kingdom from the evil Kauravas," Vyasa said to Arjuna. "Therefore, O Arjuna, you must pray to Lord Shiva and ask for divine weapons." On an auspicious day, Arjuna left for the Himalayas, to perform a penance.

He soon reached Mount Kailash, Lord Shiva's abode. As he wandered about, he saw a beautiful deer. Arjuna shot an arrow at the deer. At the same time, another arrow came from opposite direction and pierced the deer. It was a hunter's arrow. The deer lay dead with two arrows in his chest. Both Arjuna and the hunter staked their claim over the prey.

A terrible fight ensued between them. Once their arrows were exhausted, they began wrestling with each other. Arjuna was shocked to see that the hunter was defeating him at every skill. "He can't be an ordinary man!" Arjuna thought, and he was right! The hunter was none other than Lord Shiva himself. He appeared before Arjuna and granted him his most powerful divine weapon, Pashupatastra. "Use it wisely, Arjuna!" said Shiva. "I will, O Lord!" said Arjuna. Shiva also advised him to go to Lord Indra's Kingdom, Heaven, and stay there for five years. Arjuna followed Shiva's advice and went to Heaven. Indra, who was also his foster father, hugged and welcomed him.

Urvashi, a celestial nymph, taught Arjuna to dance. During the course of time, Urvashi fell in love with Arjuna and wished to marry him. But Arjuna refused, stating that he had always thought of her as a mother. Angered with his response, Urvashi cursed Arjuna. "May you live your life as a eunuch," she said. Indra then came to Arjuna's help and altered the curse, saying, "Urvashi's words shall hold good only for a year, and you may choose when that year should be."

Arjuna then returned to his brothers and Draupadi, who were still living in the forest. One day, Sage Durvasa and his disciples happened to pass through the forest. They were really hungry and saw Draupadi sitting outside her hut. At that time, none of the Pandava brothers were home. Durvasa asked Draupadi for food. Now Draupadi was in a fix as she had just finished eating and the vessel was empty. Trying to hide her embarrassment, she said, "There is a stream nearby. Please refresh yourselves while I prepare the food."

The sages left for the stream and Draupadi thought, "It is a testing time for me. Sage Durvasa is known for his anger. He may curse me if I don't give him food. But what shall I offer? My vessel is empty and will be refilled only tomorrow."

Suddenly, Draupadi remembered Krishna's promise. "He alone can help me solve my problem!" Thinking thus, Draupadi closed her eyes and began to pray to Krishna, "Help me, O Krishna!" In no time, Krishna appeared before her and said, "I will surely help you, sister. But I am hungry too. Give me something to eat."

"B...but there is no food left in the vessel," Draupadi said, worried. "Is it so?" asked Krishna. "Show me the vessel." Draupadi hesitantly showed the vessel to Krishna, who looked inside the vessel and said, "Why do you lie to me, O sister? It seems you want to hide this food from me. Hmm!" Draupadi was puzzled.

"Food!! Where... and how?" she uttered in surprise. "Your vessel is not yet empty, Draupadi!" Krishna said, with a mischievous smile on his face. "There is a grain of rice stuck to the bottom." Then, as Draupadi watched in astonishment, Krishna picked up the single grain of rice and carefully placed it in his mouth.

"Yum! Yum! Yum!" he said, chewing the single grain, as if it had filled his mouth. "He seems to be eating the most delicious food in the world," thought Draupadi. "That tasted really good, O sister!" Krishna said, burping. "My belly is full."

It was a miracle indeed! As soon as the grain of rice went into Krishna's stomach, it satiated the whole world. At the stream, Sage Durvasa and his disciples were hungry no more and continued on their way. Krishna had once again saved Draupadi from imminent disgrace. Draupadi thanked him and bade him goodbye as he left.

⁓ Bheema Meets Hanuman ⁓

With each passing day, the Pandavas were coming closer to the end of their exile. One afternoon, after finishing the regular household chores, Draupadi was sitting outside her hut. It was calm and peaceful all around. A gentle breeze made the environment even more pleasant.

Suddenly, a beautiful flower came floating on the breeze and fell near Draupadi's feet. Draupadi picked up the flower and smelt it. "Oh! What a refreshing fragrance!" she thought. "I want more of these flowers." So, she approached Bheema, as he was the one who would always fulfil her demands. Showing the flower to Bheema, Draupadi said, "Can you get me some more of these flowers?" Promising to return soon, Bheema went in search of the flowers. Of late, he had become very vain and rude. "No one is mightier than me!" he thought. On his way to get the flowers, he growled and roared to scare away the wild animals.

Now, it so happened that Lord Hanuman was meditating in the same forest. He was Bheema's elder brother as he too, was born of the Wind God, Vayu. Hanuman was aware of Bheema's vanity, so he decided to teach him a lesson. "Ho! Hum! Ho! Hum!" Bheema's mighty feet resounded as he walked. As he came nearer, Hanuman transformed himself into an old monkey and lay across his path.

When Bheema saw a monkey blocking his way, he was angry. "Why do you block my way, O monkey?" he roared. Hanuman did not budge. "Move aside, I say!" Bheema yelled again. "Don't you know who I am?" "Who are you, O brother?" Hanuman asked politely. "I am Bheema, the mighty son of Vayu!" Bheema said. "How dare you block my way?" At this, Hanuman said, "I am old and weak and cannot move. Please move my tail aside and go on your way!" Bheema grabbed Hanuman's tail to lift it. But it was so heavy that Bheema could not even move it. He tried again and again but the tail seemed stuck to the ground. Bheema was shocked.

"An ordinary monkey will not possess such strength!" Bheema thought. He bowed in front of Hanuman and said, "I accept the fact that I can't lift your tail, O great one! Now please tell me who you are?" "Didn't I address you as 'brother'?" So saying, Hanuman resumed his original form. Bheema was amazed to see the mightiest of the mighty. He promptly fell at Hanuman's feet and apologised. "I misbehaved! Please forgive me, Lord Hanuman!" said Bheema.

"I am proud of you, my younger brother," said Hanuman. "But you must never misuse your power and strength. Actual might is that which helps and protects those who are weaker than you." Bheema was humbled. He requested Hanuman to help the Pandavas regain their Kingdom from the Kauravas. Hanuman assured him that he would be present in the flag on Arjuna's chariot. After being blessed by his elder brother, Bheema proceeded on his way. Deep inside the Himalayan forests, he found the flowers that Draupadi had asked for. Bheema plucked some of them and happily returned home to Draupadi.

Yudhishthira And Yaksha

During their exile, the Pandavas helped many Brahmins and sages. One day, a Brahmin came running to them and pleaded, "A deer has carried away my staff and faggots. Can you please catch the deer and retrieve my materials? I can't kindle the sacrificial fire without my staff and faggots." The Pandavas felt it is their duty to help the Brahmin. So, they set out in search of the deer. They ran through the bushes and grooves but could not find the deer. Exhausted, they sat under a tree, and Yudhishthira sent Nakula in search of water.

Nakula found a pond some distance away and was just about to drink water when he heard a voice. "This pond belongs to me. Don't touch the water until you have answered all my questions!" said the voice, which emanated from the pond. But Nakula ignored the warning and drank the water from the pond. Instantly, he fell down and died. After a while, Sahdeva came in search of Nakula. He too, did the same thing and died.

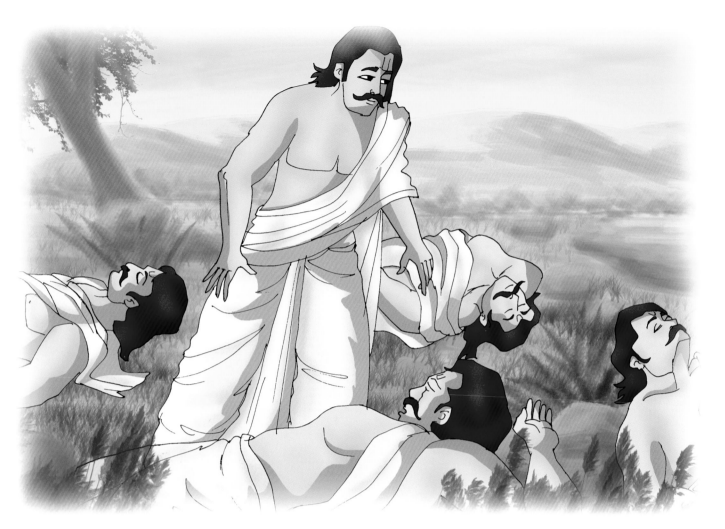

A few minutes later, Arjuna arrived at the pond. He too, was warned by the voice, but disregarding the warning, drank the water and died. Soon, Bheema too, met with the same fate. Finally, Yudhishthira arrived at the pond. Seeing his brothers lying dead, he burst into tears. Just then the voice, coming from the pond, told him how his brothers had ignored the warning and had died. "O Master of the pond," said Yudhishthira humbly, "I apologise on behalf of my brothers. Please tell me who you are."

At this, a divine figure appeared before Yudhishthira and said, "I am Yaksha, a demigod." Yaksha then asked several questions, to which Yudhishthira gave appropriate replies. Finally, the Yaksha said, "Choose one of your brothers who you would like to be restored to life." "I choose Nakula," said Yudhishthira, "because Nakula is Mother Madri's son. If Nakula lives, both my mothers will have one son alive!" Yaksha was so pleased with Yudhishthira's honesty and righteousness that he restored all his brothers to life.

~ The Pandavas In Hiding ~

Days passed into months, months rolled into years, and soon the Pandavas' twelve years of exile were over. The thirteenth year was to be spent in hiding. The Pandavas needed a secure place to spend their one year incognito. Arjuna suggested they seek refuge in the Kingdom of Matsya that lay at the outskirts of the forest. "King Virata of Matsya is very kind and generous," said Arjuna. "He will definitely help us." "But we must not forget that, if we are identified during this year, we will be exiled for another twelve years," said Bheema. "Duryodhana will leave no stone unturned to try to spot us. His men will always be on the prowl." "You are right, brother!" said Arjuna. "Let's then go in disguise, so that no one will be able to identify us!" said Arjuna. "That should be fine!" nodded Nakula and Sahdeva.

It was decided that the Pandava brothers and Draupadi would dress up as common people and ask King Virata for jobs.

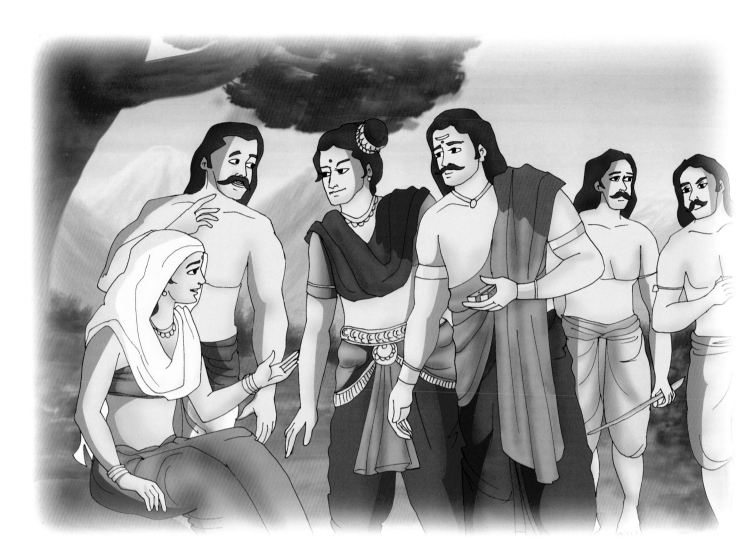

Yudhishthira was good at dice and also knew the secret skills of running a royal court. He decided to ask for the job of advising as well as entertaining the King. Bheema had but one weakness, and that was food, so he chose to become the chief cook and work in the kitchen. Arjuna, due to Urvashi's curse, was destined to pass one year as an eunuch. So, he decided to present himself as an eunuch and teach dance and music to King Virata's daughter, Princess Uttara. Nakula and Sahdeva were well trained in grooming horses and taking care of cows. They opted to work in the stable and cowshed. Draupadi decided to become the chief maid-servant to the Queen.

They changed their names, too. Yudhishthira assumed the name 'Kanka'; Bheema was called 'Ballava'; Arjuna was Brihannala; Nakula was Dharmagranthi; Sahdeva was Tantripal and Draupadi was Sairandhri. They all dressed according to their respective roles and left for the Kingdom of Matsya.

On the way, Yudhishthira cautioned his brothers, especially Bheema, not to display any of their individual characteristics as that would bring them under suspicion. "Keep your well-known anger under control, Bheema!" said Yudhishthira. "Hush! Hush! Call me 'Ballava'!" Bheema said softly. "Haha! You are right, brother!" said Yudhishthira. "We all must get into the habit of calling each other by our new names."

Soon, they reached King Virata's court. "We have come here with high hopes, Your Majesty!" said Yudhishthira. "We are homeless and jobless. Please employ us in your service, so we can earn our livelihood." King Virata thought for a while, then said, "You seem to be honest and hardworking. I will employ you in my palace." Since the Pandavas were in disguise, King Virata could not identify them. The Pandavas' plan was successful and they lived in King Virata's palace, assuming their respective roles.

Kanka was always with King Virata, assisting him in the day-to-day affairs of the State. In the evenings, he amused the King with his skills at dice.

Ballava took command of the royal kitchen. He prepared delicious dishes for the royal family. Although his hands were at work, his mind would be wandering, making plans for the future. "One year from now... and I will teach a lesson to Duryodhana and Dushasana," Ballava would think.

Brihannala taught dance to King Virata's daughter, Princess Uttara. Dharmagranthi tended the horses and Tantripal looked after the cows. Sairandhri looked after the personal needs of King Virata's wife, Queen Sudeshna. The days flew by.

One day, Queen Sudeshna's evil-minded brother, Keechaka, paid a visit to Matsya. As soon as his lustful eyes fell upon Sairandhri, he was attracted by her beauty and youthfulness.

Keechaka, then instructed his attendants to send Sairandhri with food and drinks to his chamber. When Sairandhri entered Keechaka's chamber, the wicked fellow made indecent passes at her. "O beautiful woman, will you marry me?" he asked. "I am already married!" Sairandhri replied. "To whom?" asked Keechaka. "To not one but five mighty men!" replied Sairandhri. "And they make you work like a servant! Hah!" Keechaka said mockingly. "Forget your husbands and come to me! I will treat you like a Queen!" Sairandhri was enraged and left the chamber.

That night, she secretly met Ballava in the kitchen and complained about Keechaka.

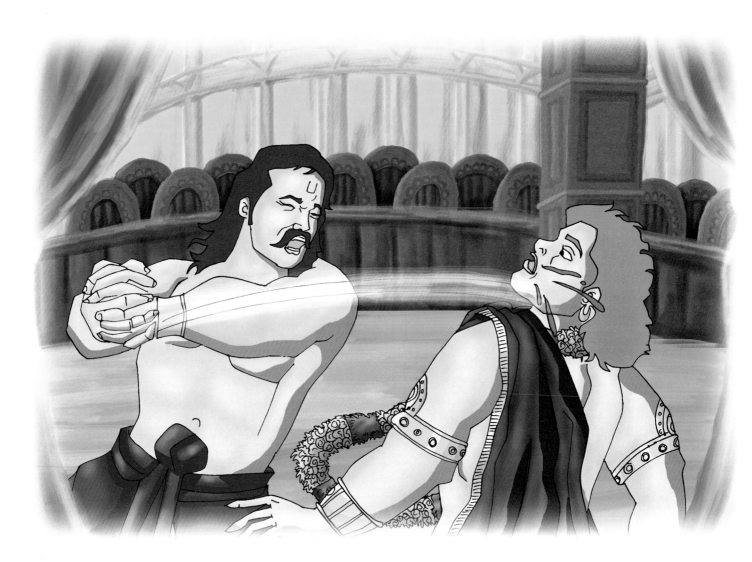

Ballava was very angry. He decided to teach Keechaka a lesson. "I have a plan, Sairandhri!" he said. "Do as I say!" Then he whispered his plan into Sairandhri's ears.

The next morning, as soon as Sairandhri saw Keechaka, she gave him an invitation. "Please come to the dance hall today evening; I shall be waiting for you." Keechaka was thrilled. "Sure, my lady!" he nodded. "I shall be there!" All was going according to Ballava's plan. In the evening, Keechaka arrived at to the dance hall. Sairandhri and Ballava were hiding behind a pillar, so Keechaka could not see them because of the darkness. "Where are you, dear Sairandhri?" he asked. "Here, behind this pillar!" replied Sairandhri. As soon as Keechaka came near the pillar, Ballava pounced upon him. Keechaka was caught unawares. Ballava whirled Keechaka round and banged him on the ground, putting him to death.

The next day, the news of Keechaka's death spread like wildfire. People were curious to see the brave man who had killed the mighty Keechaka, but no one knew how Keechaka was killed and by whom. "Keechaka was so powerful and fierce," said the courtiers to each other, "only an amazingly strong man could have killed him. Who could he be?"

Meanwhile, the news reached Hastinapur. Dushasana came running to Duryodhana's chamber and cried, "O brother Duryodhana! Did you hear, Keechaka has been killed?" "What? Keechaka... that mighty warrior has been killed?" Duryodhana shouted, not able to believe his ears. He instantly went to Shakuni. "Why are you so shocked at Keechaka's murder, dear Duryodhana?" asked Shakuni.

"I think, only one person and that is none other than Bheema, could have killed Keechaka," said Duryodhana. Does that mean that Bheema is hiding in the Kingdom of King Virata?"

"Maybe!" said Shakuni. "It is quite possible that his other brothers and his wife are also with him. "Then what are we waiting for?" Duryodhana raged. "Let's attack Virata's Kingdom and find the Pandavas, so we can send them to another twelve-year exile."

The very next day, Duryodhana led an attack on the Kingdom of Matsya. King Virata's army was not prepared for this sudden attack. On the first day of the war many soldiers of King Virata were killed.

That night King Virata was restless. "My army is no match for the huge Kaurava Army," he said to Kanka, his confidant and wellwisher. "If this continues, we will soon be defeated."

"That will never happen," Kanka interrupted. "Rest assured, King Virata! The Kauravas will have to retreat." "Really... but how is it possible?" asked Virata.

Kanka suggested, "Allow me to join your army. Ballava, Dharmagranthi and Tantripal are good warriors, too! Let them mingle with your force." Virata agreed; and so, the next morning when the war resumed, the four Pandava brothers joined Virata's army. Since they were in disguise, the Kauravas were not able to identify them. Brihannala too, joined the army as the charioteer of King Virata's son, Prince Uttar. He drove the chariot towards the enemy. As soon as Prince Uttar saw the huge Kaurava Army, he sank back in his chariot. "Oh, how will I face the mighty Kauravas!" Uttar murmured. "I don't have such sophisticated weapons as they do."

That evening, when the battle had ceased for the day, Brihannala drove Prince Uttar in his chariot into the forest. "Why are we here?" asked the Prince. "Wait and watch!" said Brihannala, smiling. Then he climbed a tree and collected all the special weapons that he had hidden.

Offering the weapons to Prince Uttar, Brihannala said, "These are Arjuna's weapons. You may need them in the war tomorrow." Prince Uttar was startled and asked, "Arjuna's weapons? How do you know about them?" "Because I am Arjuna!" said Brihannala. "But, please keep it a secret till the war ends." Prince Uttar was overjoyed. He thanked Arjuna for being with him. "I am sure we will defeat the Kauravas tomorrow," said Prince Uttar.

The next day, Arjuna dressed as Brihannala drove Prince Uttar's chariot into the battlefield. He even shot arrows at the enemy. When the Kauravas saw a woman charioteer, they could not hide their surprise. "Look at that woman charioteer!" the soldiers cried. "She is an archer too!" Prince Uttar and his army fought bravely.

Finally, the Kauravas were forced to retreat. When Prince Uttar returned victorious, King Virata was thrilled.

A thought struck his mind. "I know it is impossible for our small army to defeat the Kauravas," said Virata. "We have won only because of the support of Kanka and his companions. They are not just ordinary men! They fought like ferocious warriors!"

"You are right, father!" said Prince Uttar. "They are the Pandava brothers, the greatest warriors!" At that time the five Pandavas arrived there in their original attire. King Virata was overwhelmed that he had an opportunity to live with such great men, but at the same time, he also felt sorry for having treated them as ordinary men. "Please forgive me, O Yudhishthira," said King Virata, "if I have hurt you in any way!" Yudhishthira hugged Virata and said, "Don't embarrass me, O great King. It is not you but I, who must apologise for having lived here in disguise. Please excuse us, for we did so under compulsion. We shall be grateful to you forever, for giving us shelter."

King Virata made a humble request to Arjuna. "Please accept my daughter, Princess Uttara, as your wife!" But Arjuna refused, saying that Princess Uttara had been his disciple and so, was like a daughter to him. "Instead, O King Virata," said Arjuna, "please accept my proposal; I ask for Uttara's hand in marriage for my son, Abhimanyu!"

Virata was only too glad to accept Arjuna's proposal. He instantly ordered the ministers and priests to arrange for the grand wedding. Invitations were sent to the various Kingdoms far and wide. On an auspicious day, the beautiful Princess Uttara married the brave Prince Abhimanyu. Krishna and Balrama came to bless the couple. In the meantime, there was confusion and tension at Dhritarashtra's court. Duryodhana was not able to accept his defeat. "How could Virata's army, which consists of just a handful of men, defeat us?" he cried. "I am sure that woman charioteer and archer was Arjuna."

"You are right, brother!" nodded Dushasana. "No one else can be so skilful." Then suddenly Duryodhana laughed triumphantly, "Hahaha! That means we have identified the Pandavas during their one-year of hiding! Excellent! They will have to go into the forest for another twelve years and..."

"You are mistaken, Duryodhana!" Bheeshma intercepted. "Don't be so happy! The thirteenth year ended right before the day you spotted Arjuna. They have successfully completed their twelve years of exile and the one year of living incognito. They can go back to their Kingdom anytime now!"

"Hah! Only if I return their Kingdom to them!" cried Duryodhana. Bheeshma was angry at this; he said, "Don't forget that the Pandavas have a rightful stake in the Kingdom." "Then let them fight us and claim their stake!" said Duryodhana.

⊰ Yudhishthira's Bid For Peace ⊱

Meanwhile, in Matsya, after the marriage ceremony was over, Yudhishthira and King Virata held a conference to discuss about the future course of action. It was decided that King Virata would send his messenger to Hastinapur, to tell King Dhritarashtra that the Pandavas had fulfilled the conditions and now wanted their Kingdom back. So, a messenger of peace was sent to Hastinapur, but a proud and adamant Duryodhana refused to return Indraprastha to the Pandavas.

Arjuna went to Dwarka to seek advice and support from Krishna. When he entered Krishna's chamber, he saw that Krishna was fast asleep and Duryodhana was sitting near Krishna's head. Duryodhana also had come there to seek Krishna's support. Arjuna quietly sat at Krishna's feet. When Krishna awoke, naturally he saw Arjuna first and asked him his wish. Duryodhana objected, saying that he had arrived prior to Arjuna, but Krishna said that he had seen Arjuna first. He chose to support the Pandavas.

Duryodhana then went to Balrama, but Balrama preferred to stay away from the fight between the cousins. "I will not support either of the parties," he said. Later, he went off on a pilgrimage. When Duryodhana left Dwarka, Krishna accompanied Arjuna to Matsya. Bheema, Arjuna, Nakula and Sahdeva, were all of the opinion that they should start preparing for war. But Yudhishthira wanted to make one last bid for peace. "War brings destruction," he said. "I don't want unnecessary killing. Therefore, O Krishna, I request you to convince the Kauravas to return our Kingdom peacefully."

However, Draupadi still wanted revenge. "This Draupadi," she said, "sister of the Lord of the Universe, and wife of five brave, invincible warriors had to go through horrible disgrace! Don't forget, O Krishna, that I have to cleanse my hair only with Dushasana's blood!" At this, Krishna promised her that all the culprits would soon be punished.

Krishna went as the Pandavas' ambassador to Dhritarashtra's court. "Yudhishthira is not in favour of war, O King", said Krishna, "Be just to your brother's sons. Give them back their share of the Kingdom."

Even before Dhritarashtra could speak, his pampered son, Duryodhana shouted, "Don't plead for the Pandavas, O Krishna! No words are going to influence me. I shall not give them anything."

"Duryodhana," said Krishna. "Your irresponsible behaviour will only bring calamity to the whole clan. Save the Kingdom from annihilation. Give the Pandavas half the Kingdom, their rightful share!" "No chance!" Duryodhana cried. "Why do you waste your time, O Krishna? I won't give half the Kingdom to the Pandavas."

"Then give them at least five villages!" said Krishna.

"NEVER!" cried Duryodhana. "I won't part with even an inch of land, let alone five villages."

At this, Krishna said, "In that case, the Pandavas will be left with no option but war! Be ready for that!" "HAHAHAHAHA!" Duryodhana laughed. "Is it a warning? Why should I fear those five mosquitoes? Let them come."

"Alright, Duryodhana! You will soon regret your stubbornness. Prepare your Hastinapur to face grim consequences." So saying, Krishna left the court and returned to Matsya.

This way, Yudhishthira's last bid for peace failed as well. He was disappointed as he knew, war will not be good for the masses. But he did not have a choice. "Prepare for war!" said Krishna. "You have to establish the victory of good over evil! It's time to stand for a noble cause and fight for your rights!"

Indra And Karna

War was inevitable! Both the Kauravas and the Pandavas began to plan their respective strategies and assessed the strength and weaknesses of their opponents. While Arjuna was the best archer on the Pandavas' side, Karna was no less on the Kauravas' side. Some people even rated Karna greater than Arjuna! This fact caused great concern in the heart of Indra, Arjuna's foster father.

Up above, in the Heaven, Indra sat thinking about how to ensure Arjuna's security. He knew that Karna would be invincible as long as he had his golden armour and earrings on his body. Hence, Indra decided to rob Karna of his natural protection.

Karna was known to be very generous. Indra disguised himself as a Brahmin and approached Karna. "I have heard you never turn down anyone's request," Indra said. "I want something from you!" "What is it, O Brahmin?" asked Karna humbly. "Please tell me and it will be yours."

Indra was just waiting for this moment. He quickly said, "Please give me your golden armour and earrings!" For a moment, Karna was silent. This generosity would cost him his life, but how could the generous-hearted son of Surya refuse a Brahmin?

Karna took off his sword and in no time ripped apart his armour. Then he took off his golden earrings, too. "Here, O Brahmin!" said Karna, offering his golden armour and earrings to the Brahmin.

For a moment, nature stood still. The wind stopped blowing and the waves of the ocean froze! What had Indra done? How could he be so cruel? Seeing Karna's supreme sense of generosity, Indra felt belittled. He resumed his original form and apologised to Karna for being selfish and cunning. As a mark of gratitude, Indra gifted his most powerful weapon, called the Vasavi Shakti, to Karna. "Use it wisely, Karna!" Indra said, "It can be used only once." Then he blessed Karna and took leave.

⌁ Kunti Meets Karna ⌁

The other person worried for Arjuna's life was his mother, Kunti. She knew that Karna alone had the potential to defeat Arjuna. On the eve of the war, Kunti went to meet Karna. With a heavy heart, she told him the truth that he was her own son.

Karna was stunned. After gazing at Kunti for a while, he spoke, "Mother... O mother! Why did you abandon me when I needed you the most?" Kunti burst into tears. "I know, I have been unjust to you," she said. "But I was helpless, O son! Today, the culprit is before you. Forgive me, if you can, or else punish me in whichever way you like." Hearing this, Karna too, burst into tears. "Don't say that, mother!" he said. "All my life, I have been searching for my mother. You were in front of my eyes but I couldn't recognise you. But why did you stay away from me when you knew I was your son?" Kunti did not have any answer to Karna's innocent questions. It was a touching moment.

After some time, Kunti pleaded with Karna, "Arjuna is your brother... your own younger brother. Please don't look at him as your enemy. Spare his life, I beg! Join the Pandavas in the war!"

"It's too late, O mother!" said Karna. "Where were you when your sons were mocking me, calling me 'sutaputra'? Why didn't you tell them that day that I was their elder brother? Today when their life is in danger, you have come to remind me that they are my brothers. Now I don't recognise any relationship other than friendship, the one that saved my honour at the hour of my humiliation. I am indebted to Duryodhana and shall never betray his trust. Arjuna shall always be my enemy. However, I promise you that I won't kill any of your other four sons. Either I will kill Arjuna or be killed by him. In any case, you will remain a mother of five sons: either Karna or Arjuna."

With a sad heart and heavy steps, Kunti returned to her palace.

⁓ The War ⁓

The Mahabharata War was announced. It was to be the greatest Dharma-Yuddha* of all times. Rules and regulations were laid down. War would be fought from dawn to dusk. Injured and weaponless warriors would not be attacked. The fight would be between equals; a charioteer would take on another charioteer, while a pedestrian would attack another pedestrian. No one was to attack anyone from behind. At sunset, the warriors would return to their respective camps. The injured would be treated by the physicians. Anyone from one camp could visit the other camp after sunset.

As the day dawned, both the armies marched towards the battlefield, Kurukshetra. All around, there were sounds of war drums, trumpets, conches and the clank of weapons. Each side had the support of many Kings. Grandsire Bheeshma was the commander-in-chief of the Kaurava Army, while Drishtidyumna took command of the Pandava Army.

*War of righteousness

Krishna had decided not to participate in the war. However, he was present as Arjuna's charioteer. Conches were blown to mark the beginning of the war. Krishna held the reigns of Arjuna's chariot and awaited his command.

Arjuna threw a last-minute glance at the huge Kaurava Army. Bheeshma, Drona, Duryodhana, and all the others stood at attention. Suddenly, Arjuna thought, "Oh, these are the warriors I am going to fight against! But they are my own people."

Seeing Arjuna silent, Krishna asked, "What's the matter, Arjuna?" "I can't fight, O Krishna!" said Arjuna in a trembling voice. "I am going to kill my own people! Grandsire Bheeshma, Guru Drona, Guru Kripacharya... all are my revered ones. How can I raise weapons against them? My uncles, my cousins, my friends, and loved ones... How will I shoot arrows at them?" So saying, Arjuna sank back in his chariot.

Krishna was startled. "You can't do this at this time, Arjuna," he cried. "The battle has begun. There's no time to sink and sulk. Get hold of your Gandiva and attack!"

"It's heartbreaking, O Krishna!" Arjuna sobbed. "How can I kill the ones whom I have lived with. They are my own..." "No, they are not!" Krishna interrupted. "Only your duties are your own at this point of time. Get up, O great warrior, and fight."

"Against whom shall I fight?" asked Arjuna. "All around I can see my only relatives."

"Don't think of them as your relatives, Arjuna!" said Krishna. "Think of them as evil people. Your duty is to fight against evil." Krishna's inspiring words had no effect on Arjuna. Krishna then blessed Arjuna with divine eyes to see the Cosmic Form of the Lord.

A spark of light emitted from Krishna's palm and fell upon Arjuna's eyes. "Awake, Arjuna," said Krishna, "and see the Eternal Truth!"

As Arjuna opened his eyes, he saw the brightest of bright, the greatest of great and the holiest of holy, the Almighty in his Universal Form. At that point of time, Arjuna could witness what no one else ever did. The Supreme Lord was all-pervasive.

"I am the Eternal Truth!" said the Lord. "Whenever there is a decline of righteousness, and injustice is on the rise, then I incarnate! For the protection of the virtuous, for the destruction of evil-doers, and to establish Dharma* on this earth, I am born from age to age. The world is but transitional. It transits from the past to present and from the present to future. Nothing remains as it is. All comes from me and all returns to me. What is here today will not be there tomorrow. That is the essence of the Universe."

*Righteousness

"Own not what you get; mourn not what you lose; for nothing belongs to you and you belong to nothing. You have arrived in this world empty-handed and so shall you leave. The one who is born today shall die tomorrow. The world is only a place to perform your duties. You are only a means to carry out the Divine Orders. Celebrate not your victory; regret not your defeat; for whatever happens is by the Divine Order and is for your good."

Arjuna listened spellbound as the Lord spoke, "If you kill your enemy, you are actually killing only his body and not his soul. Soul is beyond birth and death; no weapon can destroy it, no fire can burn it; neither can air blow it, nor can water drench it. So, O Arjuna, don't be depressed. You are not sinning, but only obeying my orders. Awake and arise! Your duty calls you!"

The sermon that Krishna gave to Arjuna is known as The Gita.

Inspired and enlightened by Krishna's words, Arjuna arose in his chariot. "Pick up the Gandiva, O mighty warrior!" Krishna commanded. "Fight for the triumph of good over evil." "I will, O Lord!" responded Arjuna, with all his zeal and zest.

Meanwhile, the Kaurava Army was bewildered. "What's happening on the Pandavas' side?" the Kaurava soldiers whispered. "Are they scared of us?" Suddenly, the battlefield reverberated with the twang of Arjuna's bowstring. The Pandava Army cheered Arjuna.

The war had begun, with Bheeshma, Krishna, Arjuna and others blowing their conches. On the first day, the huge Kaurava Army far outnumbered the handful of Pandavas. At sunset, the war had to be stopped as per the rules laid out. Krishna blew his conch and marked the end of the day's battle. All the soldiers retreated to their camps.

That night, the Pandavas were worried. Many of their soldiers had been killed on the very first day. On the second day, Arjuna took command of his army and arranged his men in a special format, which gave little scope to the Kauravas to advance and attack the Pandavas. But nothing could stop the skillful Bheeshma. He killed many warriors, including King Virata's son, Uttar.

Nine days passed in this way. It seemed the war would never come to an end. Bheeshma and Dronacharya had destroyed many great Pandava warriors. As the day's battle closed, Krishna called for a meeting with Arjuna and Yudhishthira. "If Bheeshma is allowed to continue, we will soon be defeated," said Krishna. He advised Arjuna to make use of Shikhandi, the brave warrior who was born a woman, as a shield and attack Bheeshma.

The next day, Bheeshma was on his usual rampage. Arjuna, with Shikhandi standing in front of him as a shield, approached Bheeshma.

As soon as Bheeshma saw Shikhandi, he lowered his bow, as he had vowed not to fight against women. Arjuna took advantage of Bheeshma's dilemma and began to shoot arrows at him. In no time, innumerable arrows pierced Bheeshma's body. The great warrior fell down and lay there as if lying on a bed of arrows. Just at that time, the conch was blown to mark the end of the day's battle. All the warriors gathered around Bheeshma.

All hatred disappeared in that moment of personal loss from the Kauravas and Pandavas alike. Bheeshma called Arjuna and said, "You have given me a bed of arrows. But my head hangs in the air. Please give me a pillow." Arjuna, crying bitterly, shot three arrows below Bheeshma's head to give him support. "I am thirsty, O Arjuna!" said Bheeshma. "Bring my mother Ganga to me." Arjuna shot an arrow into the earth, and Ganga sprang up from the earth and water started directly pouring into the Bheeshma's mouth. Arjuna then knelt before his beloved Grandsire and wept.

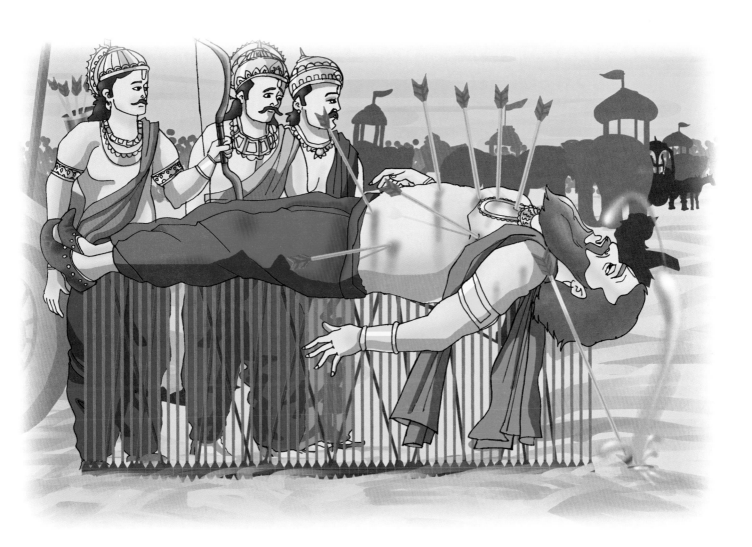

Bheeshma had the boon to choose the time of his death. Since the sun was in southern hemisphere at that time, he did not wish to give up his body. He desired to be shifted to one corner of the battlefield where he lay on his bed of arrows, alone, waiting for an auspicious moment to set his soul free.

The day dawned and the war continued. Now Drona took command of the Kaurava Army. His main aim was to check Abhimanyu, who had killed many Kaurava soldiers on the previous day. But no matter how hard Drona tried, he could not stand in Abhimanyu's way. The young warrior's arrows flew faster than lightning. By the end of the twelfth day's battle, Abhimanyu had killed great warriors like Alambusa and Paurava. That night, when Duryodhana and Drona sat down to plan the next day's strategy, Duryodhana said, "Abhimanyu can kill all of us single-handedly. We must get rid of him." Drona had the capability to defeat the Pandavas, but he feared Arjuna.

"If someone can engage Arjuna on another front, I can defeat the Pandavas," said Drona. "Fine then!" said Duryodhana. "We have five warriors, the Samsaptakas, who have sworn either to win or die in the battle. I will instruct them to attack Arjuna and keep him engaged till you finish the job."

So, on the thirteenth day, the Samsaptakas attacked Arjuna and kept him engaged on another front. Meanwhile, Drona arranged his army in a Chakravyuha* formation. When Yudhishthira saw this, he was terribly worried. Only Krishna, his son Pradyumna and Arjuna knew how to break the Chakravyuha. Unfortunately, none of them was present at the time.

Seeing Yudhishthira worried, Abhimanyu came forward and said, "Give me a chance, O Uncle! I know how to pierce the Chakravyuha!" As a child in his mother's womb, Abhimanyu had heard the narration but only half. So, he did not know how to come out of the Chakravyuha.

*Chakra meaning circle and Vyuha meaning formation.

Yudhishthira hesitated to send Abhimanyu into the tricky formation, but he had no other option. "Don't worry, O Uncle," assured brave Abhimanyu. "Let me pave the way first; then you all can follow." Yudhishthira agreed to this and asked Abhimanyu to proceed.

Abhimanyu charged at the Kaurava Army. Fighting skillfully, he broke the first layer of the Chakravyuha. As fate would have it, Yudhishthira and the others could not follow him into the Chakravyuha. Their way was blocked by King Jayadratha, who had a boon from Lord Shiva that he could, for one day, hold back all the Pandavas, except Arjuna. Without Arjuna around, the Pandavas could not stand against Jayadratha.

Meanwhile, Abhimanyu penetrated the innermost layer of the Chakravyuha and stood alone, in front of the wicked Kauravas. But this son of Arjuna and nephew of Krishna knew no fear.

Like an enraged elephant, he kept annihilating the enemy soldiers. The Kaurava Army was terrified and began to flee. Duryodhana tried to stop his soldiers from running away, but in vain.

Abhimanyu single-handedly took on great warriors like Drona, Kripacharya, Karna, Ashwatthama, Brihadbala and Kritavarma. Finally, Duryodhana instructed his men to attack Abhimanyu all together at once, breaking the rule of one to one.

Karna broke Abhimanyu's bow. Abhimanyu then began to fight with his sword and shield. But soon Drona and Karna broke his shield too. Now Abhimanyu pulled off his chariot-wheel and whirled it in the air. He fought bravely, but he did not know how to come out of the Chakravyuha. All his weapons were either exhausted or broken. Arjuna's son was trapped! And that was what the Kauravas wanted. Taking advantage of the situation, six Kaurava warriors attacked him at the same time and killed him.

There was shock and grief in the Pandavas' camp. When Arjuna returned and learnt how the Kauravas had used deceit to kill Abhimanyu, he flew into a rage. "How cruel could one be?" he cried. "All of them attacked a single warrior? That too, when he had no weapon for his defense!! Shameful!"

Krishna comforted Arjuna and said, "Don't cry, Arjuna! Our Abhimanyu died a true warrior's death. His name shall ever be engraved in history. The Kauravas will soon have to pay for his gruesome murder." But, Arjuna was not convinced and at that moment, he took a vow, "Tomorrow, before the sun sets, I will kill Jayadratha or else give up my life by burning myself."

The next day, Jayadratha was terrified. He sought protection from Duryodhana and said, "I had the power to defeat the Pandavas only for a day. Today, I am sure the Pandavas will find and kill me."

"We are there to protect you, O brother-in-law!" Duryodhana assured Jayadratha. He then ordered the Kaurava Army to encircle Jayadratha's chariot. Arjuna tried to attack Jayadratha but failed, as Jayadratha was almost invisible. Soon, it was afternoon! The Pandavas feared that if Arjuna could not kill Jayadratha before sunset, he might set himself on fire. Just then, the sky became dark, and the stars came up on the horizon. "Victory! Victory!" shouted the Kauravas. "Arjuna's vow is broken; he will have to die now! The day's battle has ended!"

Jayadratha heaved a sigh of relief and began to dance with joy. Suddenly, the day became bright again! Actually, it had become dark because of a total solar eclipse at that hour and not because the sun had set! As soon as the eclipse ended, the sun came out. In that light, Arjuna spotted Jayadratha. "Shoot, Arjuna!" Krishna cried. Arjuna's arrow flew towards Jayadratha and hacked off his head. Out of anger and vengeance, the Kauravas did not halt the war even after sunset. They continued to fight in the dark.

Now Krishna thought of a plan. He called Bheema aside and said, "It's time to summon your gigantic and powerful son Ghatotkacha! With his supernatural powers, he can enlarge or shorten his body and can also become invisible." Bheema closed his eyes and thought of Ghatotkacha. Instantly, as promised, the obedient son appeared before his father. "O Ghatotkacha! Show your might and annihilate the Kauravas!" Bheema ordered. Ghatotkacha began to vomit fire and throw a large quantity of sand and boulders on the Kauravas.

None of their lethal weapons could harm the giant warrior. There was total chaos in the Kauravas' camp. "If this continues, none of us will remain alive!" Duryodhana thought, worried. He requested Karna to kill Ghatotkacha using the Vasavi Shakti that Indra had given him. Karna had preserved the one-time-use weapon for Arjuna, but he had to use it on Ghatotkacha to save the Kauravas. Thus, the loyal son of Bheema died, but saved Arjuna's life, which was very precious for the Pandavas.

The next day, when the war resumed, Drona seemed almost invincible. Like a fierce storm, he swept away all that came in his way. Krishna called Yudhishthira aside and said, "If we let Drona continue in this manner, he will soon kill all of us. I have a plan by which we can make Drona give up his bow. In our army, there is an elephant named Ashwatthama. Drona has a son by the same name. We will kill the elephant and then make an announcement that Ashwatthama is dead. I am sure when Drona hears this, he will give up fighting."

"No...I can't lie!" Yudhishthira said. "It's not fair." "Oh, was it fair when six cruel men slaughtered Abhimanyu?" Krishna retorted. "If they can resort to deceit, why shouldn't we? Moreover, you are not telling a lie. You are just mentioning a half-truth." Finally, Yudhishthira agreed.

The Pandavas killed the elephant Ashwatthama. Yudhishthira cried out, "ASHWATTHAMA IS DEAD! Either the man or the elephant."

Drona was shocked to hear this. He knew Yudhishthira would never lie. "What did you say, Yudhishthira?" Drona asked.

Yudhishthira again cried, "ASHWATTHAMA IS DEAD; either the man or the elephant." He spoke the second half of the sentence very softly. Moreover, the deafening sound of clanking weapons, trumpeting elephants and neighing horses made it really difficult for Drona to understand what Yudhishthira had uttered. All that he could hear was ASHWATTHAMA IS DEAD!

Drona's heart sank. "My son... O Ashwatthama... how can I believe you are no more?" Heartbroken, Drona fell from his chariot. He did not wish to live any more. Seeing this, Drishtidyumna shot an arrow at Drona and killed him. It is said that much before Drishtidyumna's arrow pierced Drona's body, his soul had already departed.

After Drona's death, Karna was appointed the new commander-in-chief of the Kaurava Army. The son of Surya rode forth in his magnificent chariot. Seeing his arch enemy approaching, Arjuna asked Krishna to ride forward. "Be alert, Arjuna!" cried Karna. The two mighty archers were now face to face. Both had vowed to kill each other. Karna began to shoot arrow after arrow at Arjuna, but Arjuna had an antidote for each one of them.

Suddenly, Karna shot his Nagastra* at Arjuna. The arrow spewed fire as it raced towards Arjuna. It could have been fatal to Arjuna, but Krishna skillfully lowered the chariot into the mud by a few inches, so Arjuna escaped the arrow.

Just then, Karna's chariot wheel got stuck in the mud. He jumped off and tried to pull it out. At that moment, Arjuna aimed an arrow at Karna.

*A serpent-like divine arrow

"Wait!" Karna cried. "You should not do that! According to war ethics, one should not attack a defenseless person."

"Those words don't sound good coming from your mouth, O Karna!" Arjuna said. "Why didn't you follow ethics when Abhimanyu was trapped in your Chakravyuha? Where was your sensibility when all of you attacked a warrior, who was defenseless and wounded?"

Karna knew he was in trouble. He reached for his most powerful weapon, the Brahmastra*. The Brahmastra could be used only by chanting a sacred verse.

Just as Karna was about to chant the verse to invoke the Brahmastra, he forgot the verse. Parashurama's curse came true and Karna's knowledge deserted him at the most crucial hour. Taking advantage of the situation, Arjuna shot an arrow and killed Karna.

*Is an arrow created by Brahma.

Duryodhana was aghast. "My last hope is lost!" he cried. "Only Karna was capable of defeating Arjuna. O Karna... my beloved friend! How will I live without you?"

Seeing Duryodhana shattered, his warriors started running away from the battlefield. "Our leader has lost hope; why should we risk our lives?" they grumbled. "Let us escape before the enemy captures us."

"You cowards... come back!" Duryodhana yelled out to his fleeing warriors. But his meek voice did not have the desired effect on them. One after the other, all the Kaurava warriors were killed. The Pandavas knew they were almost victorious.

But Bheema was still not satisfied. He had vowed to kill Dushasana and Duryodhana. How could he call himself victorious without fulfilling the promise he had once made to Draupadi!

So, all of a sudden, Bheema charged at Dushasana and knocked him down with one blow of his mace. Before Dushasana could get up, Bheema tore open his chest. Blood started flowing down as Dushasana lay on the ground. "This is for having touched Draupadi's veil!" he cried in anger and disgust. "I will wash Draupadi's hair in your blood!" He then collected some blood and kept it for Draupadi.

After thus killing Dushasana, Bheema turned towards Duryodhana. A terrible fight ensued between the two fierce warriors. Both Duryodhana and Bheema used the mace to fight fiercely. When Duryodhana took up a club, Bheema also attacked him with a club. Both were well built and adept in the skills of fighting.

In the end, Bheema overpowered Duryodhana, broke his thighs, and cried, "This is for humiliating Draupadi!" Duryodhana was left there to die a slow and undignified death. With this, the eighteen-day war came to an end. The Pandavas stood victorious. It was a great victory of good over evil.

The Victorious Pandavas Return To Hastinapur

When the Pandavas, accompanied by Krishna, returned to Hastinapur, they received a warm welcome. All around there were cheers of "Hail Krishna", "Hail Pandavas", and "Hail the righteous ones!" People rejoiced and celebrated the victory of good over evil. But there was one man who did not join in the celebrations, and that was none other than King Dhritarashtra. He was seething with anger and hatred for Bheema, who had killed his favourite son, Duryodhana.

Meanwhile, the Pandavas arrived at the palace and straightaway wanted to go to Dhritarashtra's chamber to receive his blessings. They were unaware of the King's fury. But Krishna was aware of his fury. Hence, before the Pandavas could reach there, Krishna placed Bheema's statue in front of the blind King. Dhritarashtra on the pretense of hugging the statue, thinking it was Bheema himself, crushed the statue with all his might and cried, "Take this for having killed my Duryodhana!" The statue crumbled to pieces under Dhritarashtra's pressure.

Just then, the Pandavas arrived. Seeing Bheema's crumbled statue, they instantly realised the cause. Krishna smiled at them and asked them to stay silent. Then he counseled Dhritarashtra. "Bheema has just done his duty, O King! The Pandavas have fought for their rights. Step into their shoes and try to understand how cruel your son, Duryodhana, had been towards them."

One by one, the Pandavas fell at Dhritarashtra's feet, asking for forgiveness. "Never was I in favour of war," said Yudhishthira, "but I had to resort to it to defeat evil." "Anyone in your place would have done the same, O son!" said Dhritarashtra, realising that Duryodhana had been punished for his own sinful deeds. "It was my fault that I overlooked his mistakes." Gandhari lamented over the death of her hundred sons. Later, she forgave the Pandavas and congratulated Kunti on having such dutiful and righteous sons, but even as she spoke, her voice was choked.

Kunti was glad to see her five sons back, but on the other hand, she mourned the death of her eldest son, Karna. Things settled down in a couple of days. Now the priests advised the King to prepare for the coronation of Yudhishthira. In a simple ceremony, Yudhishthira was crowned King of Hastinapur. His brothers supported him in the day-to-day affairs of the State.

Some years later, Dhritarashtra, Gandhari and Kunti renounced their royal life and retired into the forest, to lead a peaceful, austere life. They lived in a hermitage, in the lap of Mother Nature, and spent their days in meditation and penance, but one day their hermitage caught fire and they died.

Yudhishthira ruled wisely for many years. He established the rule of dharma and justice. Once again, truth, peace and prosperity were ushered into Hastinapur.

≈ The Pandavas' Journey To Heaven ≈

Much later, the Pandavas heard that their beloved Krishna had left his mortal body and returned to heaven. Arjuna's grief knew no bounds. Raising his hands in despair, he cried, "My best friend, confidant and guru has left this world! How and why do I live?"

Draupadi could not bear the loss of her beloved brother, Krishna, and wished to renounce this world. Yudhishthira also was of the same opinion. "I have performed my duties towards my Kingdom and family," he said. "Now my soul longs to withdraw from this world. "Why should we live then?" thought Bheema, Nakula and Sahdeva, so they decided to begin their journey to heaven.

On an auspicious day, Yudhishthira passed on his crown to Abhimanyu's son, Parikshit, who was now mature enough to rule. The five Pandava brothers and Draupadi then renounced their royal life and left for the Himalayas, the gateway to heaven.

When they were crossing a forest, a dog silently started to follow them. After a few miles, all of a sudden, Draupadi fell down and died. Though the Pandavas felt sad, they went on.

They crossed some more miles, then Sahdeva fell dead. Yudhishthira's heart ached but he quickly overcame his emotions. "Let's move on, brothers!" he said. Bheema, Arjuna and Nakula followed Yudhishthira, and so did the dog! Like a devoted disciple, the dog quietly walked behind Yudhishthira.

Hardly had they walked a few miles when Nakula fell dead, too. Arjuna froze for a moment, but soon recovered. Having renounced the world and worldly desires, they had risen above sorrow, pain and suffering. Now Bheema, Arjuna and Yudhishthira carried on their journey, with the dog faithfully following them. After a few more miles, Arjuna perished, too.

Yudhishthira and Bheema turned around, looked at their beloved brother a last time, took a deep breath and moved on. Another couple of miles later, Bheema also fell down and died.

Yudhishthira paused for a moment and prayed for his dead brothers and wife. Then he resumed his journey. Had the dog not been there, Yudhishthira would have been all alone. "He is my sincere companion!" Yudhishthira thought, looking at the dog.

Together they walked along the winding path, crossed forests, waded through streams and braved many difficulties. Finally, they reached the Himalayan mountains.

All of a sudden, Yudhishthira saw Lord Indra in his chariot appearing from the clouds. Indra's chariot stopped near Yudhishthira. "I am blessed, O Lord, to be able to see you!" said Yudhishthira, bowing.

"I am pleased with you, O Yudhishthira!" said Indra. "You have walked a long way and must be tired. I have come to take you to Heaven. Board my chariot!"

Yudhishthira got into the chariot. Then he turned around and beckoned to the dog to board the chariot.

"Who is that?" asked Indra. "He is my companion!" replied Yudhishthira.

"I am afraid you can't take him along," said Indra, frowning. "But I won't leave him either!" said Yudhishthira. "He has followed me like a true devotee. How can I desert him? My own brothers and wife left me midway. But this dog remained with me and saw me through the thorny forests and rocky mountains. Will it not be selfish of me to sit in your chariot and leave this dog to wander alone here? Please allow him to come with me."

But Indra refused to listen to Yudhishthira's pleadings. "You alone may be taken to Heaven, O Yudhishthira!" he said. "How can I allow this dog to share your good fortune?"

"Then I don't desire good fortune!" said Yudhishthira. "What good is such fortune that brings suffering and sorrow to others? Forgive me, O Lord! I may have to disobey your orders. If this dog can't come into your chariot then, I too, prefer to walk. I don't wish to go to Heaven without him. You can punish me in whichever way you like. But I cannot abandon this dog."

So saying, Yudhishthira got off Indra's chariot. At that moment, the dog was transformed into Yudhishthira's Godfather, Lord Dharma, the God of truth and justice.

Yudhishthira was surprised. He knelt before Dharma and touched his feet. Dharma blessed him and said, "I was just testing you, O son! I am pleased at your wisdom and sense of justice. A man as humble and kind as you has secured a place in Heaven."

Indra was surprised at Yudhishthira's selflessness. "While the evildoers thrive for a seat beside me, you, O noble Yudhishthira, are willing to forego your seat in Heaven! Such supreme sacrifice shall ever be admired!"

He then smiled at Yudhishthira and called him into his chariot. Dharma and Yudhishthira boarded Indra's chariot and were taken to Heaven.

As they reached the gates, Dharma and Indra suddenly disappeared. Yudhishthira stood at the gates. When he peeped in, he saw Duryodhana seated on a royal chair. It was dark all around. Yudhishthira was puzzled as to which way to go.

Then, he heard a divine voice that said, "Welcome, Yudhishthira! Walk in... this way..." "Where are my brothers and Draupadi?" asked Yudhishthira. "They are in Hell!" replied the divine voice. "Then I too, wish to go to Hell!" said Yudhishthira. "Please take me to my brothers and wife, wherever they may be!"

Just then, Dharma and Indra appeared again before Yudhishthira. "That was your final test, O son," said Dharma, "and you have successfully passed it. You will be taken to Heaven now." "But I want to go to Hell, to live with my brothers and wife," said Yudhishthira. At this, Indra smiled and said, "This is Hell, and you were brought here for a day because you told a lie. Your brothers and Draupadi are in Heaven." Indra then led Yudhishthira to Heaven. The five righteous Pandavas and their chaste wife thereafter enjoyed heavenly bliss.

Here ends the story – The Mahabharata – but the saga still lives on!